'I really wish y
mind.'

'About what?' Clint asked.

'Whether you want to yell at me or make love to me.'

'That's easy. I want to do both. Yell at you.' Feeling that unbidden pull, he leaned down and cupped Sunny's cheek in his palm. 'And then I want to make love with you.'

His touch stimulated those strange, edgy, wonderful feelings all over again. 'Don't you believe in a middle ground?'

'The middle ground's for people who don't know what they want.'

'And you do?'

'You bet.' His thumb traced around her mouth. 'I want you.'

**JoAnn Ross is also the author of these novels
in *Temptation*®**

NEVER A BRIDE
FOR RICHER OR POORER
THREE GROOMS AND A WEDDING
PRIVATE PASSIONS
THE OUTLAW
UNTAMED
WANTED!

AMBUSHED

BY

JOANN ROSS

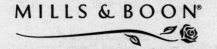

*All the characters in this book have no existence outside the imagination
of the author, and have no relation whatsoever to anyone bearing the same
name or names. They are not even distantly inspired by any individual
known or unknown to the author, and all the incidents are pure invention.*

*First published in Great Britain 1997
by Harlequin Mills & Boon Limited,
Eton House, 18-24 Paradise Road, Richmond, Surrey TW9 1SR*

© JoAnn Ross 1996

ISBN 0 263 80626 X

21-9710

*Printed and bound in Great Britain
by Caledonian International Book Manufacturing Ltd, Glasgow*

1

CLINT GARVEY SAT in the dark, calmly drinking from a bottle of Jim Beam as he methodically cleaned the antique gun he'd decided to use to end his life.

The single action Colt revolver was known by many names; the Peacemaker and the Gun That Won the West were two of the more popular. It had belonged to Clint's great-great-grandfather, Captain William Garvey.

Captain Garvey, who'd distinguished himself fighting in Union blue during the Civil War, had returned home at the end of the war only to discover that his wife had died of a fever the night before his arrival.

"Timing," Clint muttered as he traced the specialized engraving on the wooden grip of the revolver with a fingertip, "is everything."

He shook his head as he thought about the cruel twist of fate that had allowed a man to survive years of carnage without so much as a single scratch, then took the life of the woman who'd remained the single fixed star in his firmament during those brutal war years.

He imagined how William must have felt riding home, excited about being alive, excited about resuming his life, tending his cattle, making love, having children. Although there were more than a hundred years between them, Clint could definitely identify with his ancestor.

It hadn't been that long ago he'd been planning a future with the woman he loved. He looked through the alcohol fog at a framed photograph on the table beside him, depicting a laughing, auburn-haired woman. The picture of Laura Swann Fletcher had been taken during an idyllic stolen weekend in the Shenandoah Valley. That same weekend their child had been conceived. The child he hadn't even known she was carrying until they were dead.

Murdered.

The word tolled heavily in his mind, like a funeral knell. There was no escaping it. And, since the killer had thoughtlessly left him to live with the pain of such gut-wrenching loss, Clint had decided that the only thing to do was to finish the job himself.

He pulled the hammer back with his thumb. At the first click, the cylinder rotated freely, allowing him to load the single bullet. He pulled the hammer to its fully cocked position, then stuck the seven and a half inch barrel into his mouth.

Unwilling to consider this final act cowardly, Clint refused to close his eyes. Instead, he kept his gaze firmly fixed on Laura's lovely, lovely face as he pulled the trigger.

"IN ALL THE thousands of years I have been in this position, I can't remember—ever—witnessing a more dismal romantic match." The older woman's raven black eyes expressed intense disapproval as she glared over the top of her wire-framed reading glasses at the young woman standing in front of her desk. "Whatever were you thinking of?"

"I truly believed it would work," Sunny said quietly. Although it was difficult not to squirm beneath the laser-like glare she managed to hold her ground. She was, however, twisting her hands together behind her back.

Those censorious eyes widened with disbelief. "You actually believed a worldly prince and a naive young kindergarten teacher would have anything in common?"

Sunny had heard this same criticism for years and couldn't understand why she was being reprimanded for her mistake yet again. Although she was sorely tempted to point out that the criteria for the royal match had not been all that simple—there were not, after all, many eligible virgins in the latter half of the twentieth century to choose from—she managed to hold her tongue.

"It worked for Cinderella," she murmured.

"Cinderella was an exception." The words were shot at her like stones. "And she was fortunate enough to have a world-class fairy godmother. You are not," the deep voice turned heavy with scorn, "even approaching Harmony's league."

The insult, although unfortunately true, stung. Sunny knew she'd made a tactical mistake in bringing up Harmony. The woman was, without a doubt, the most famous fairy godmother who'd ever lived.

Harmony had retired after her sterling success with Cinderella and in her honor a statue of her, turning the white mice into horses for the famed pumpkin coach, had been erected in the contemplation garden.

Although Harmony was a role model for all fairy godmothers, young and old, Sunny managed, just barely, to refrain from mentioning that even she had been wise enough to realize she couldn't top her success with that pretty, albeit vapid, little scullery maid.

And if she couldn't, Sunny thought dejectedly, how in the world was anyone else expected to?

"I really don't know what we're going to do with you, Sunny," her superior, Andromeda, said with a deep, heartfelt sigh. "I realize you professed a desire to work in romance, however, I've been thinking that perhaps some other area—"

"Oh, please, don't transfer me!" Sunny untangled her fingers from behind her back and pressed her hands against her heart, which had suddenly begun to pound with a wild, out-of-control beat. "I love romance!"

"I know, dear." The dark eyes softened with affection. "You are, without a doubt, the most romantic soul we've had working here since Harmony's time. And we've all been hoping that your skills would catch up with your heart, but that doesn't seem to be happening. Does it?"

Sunny's mind quickly flicked through the couples she'd matched in the past. Surely she could find one winner to prove her competence and keep her job. The first couple who came to mind were Devil Anse Hatfield and Rose-anna McCoy. Putting aside the depressing decades-long murderous mountain feud, she tried again.

The memory of Henry VIII and Anne Boleyn was definitely not encouraging. Then there'd been that dashing soldier Antony. He and Cleopatra had seemed to be such a perfect love match. Who could have ever predicted things would turn out so tragically?

Sunny sighed. "I see your point," she said reluctantly.

"Hollyhock needs someone to help in the kitchen," Andromeda said thoughtfully. "You do seem to enjoy cooking—"

"Cooking is an avocation," Sunny interrupted. "Romance is my life!"

Andromeda frowned and continued. "What about accounting? You have an amazing knack for numbers, and we've been running so over budget lately in so many areas—"

"I'd go crazy sitting in front of a computer all day," Sunny complained. A transfer to accounting would also preclude visits to earth; unlike other fairy godmothers who found the planet uncivilized and untidy, Sunny had always thought it exhilarating and fascinating.

She dragged a trembling hand through her wild tangle of long blond curls. "I'll admit that my record has been less than stellar, but if I could only have another chance, I just know I could get things right."

Her voice trembled, she felt the traitorous sting of tears behind her eyes and Sunny, who'd been named for her unfailingly cheerful disposition, had to bite her lip to keep from weeping.

"That's precisely what we're going to give you," Andromeda surprised Sunny by saying. "One more chance."

"Oh, thank you!" When she rushed joyfully toward the desk, planning to hug her superior, she was stopped in her tracks by an uplifted hand.

"It is not a simple assignment."

"I don't care. I promise, I'll succeed." Hope sang its clear sweet song in her veins. "And if I don't, you can transfer me out of romance forever."

"That's our intention." Andromeda's tone assured Sunny that this truly was her final chance to prove that she could make a successful love match. "The man we're assigning you to will not be cooperative."

"That's all right—"

"Indeed, I expect he will fight you at every turn. You see, he has already loved once. And that love was so strong and so deep that he's convinced himself it can never be equaled."

"That's so sad." Ever the optimist, Sunny couldn't imagine such a defeatist attitude. "What happened? Did she leave him for another man?"

"She died."

"That is tragic."

"It's worse. Laura Swann Fletcher was murdered. She was also pregnant with this man's child at the time. And married to another man, a very important, very influential man. It was quite the scandal. Especially when Clint Garvey was arrested for her murder."

"Oh, dear." Sunny began to feel just the slightest twinge of worry. "That's his name? Clint?" It was a nice name, she thought. Strong and masculine. And very mortal.

"Yes. And now, as you'll see, he believes he no longer has any reason to live." She handed Sunny a thick folder. "This is their story. You'll want to acquaint yourself with the particulars."

"I'll read it right away."

"That would be advisable, in most cases. But I fear you don't have much time."

Andromeda picked up the remote control from the desktop and pointed it at the wall. Sunny watched as a picture appeared.

Clint Garvey was certainly a handsome enough man, she thought, in a rough-hewn sort of way. He was sitting down, but judging from the long legs, stretched out in front of him she suspected he'd be tall. He was whipcord lean, but his body appeared to be all muscle and sinew. The grim brackets on either side of his mouth suggested that his heart was as hard as his body. And no wonder, she thought sadly, thinking of what he'd lost.

His face, weathered from years of working outdoors was as dark as walnuts, a startling contrast to his ice blue eyes. And the bleak expression in those eyes, as he picked up the photograph of a smiling woman she took to be his beloved Laura, tore at something very deep and very elemental inside Sunny.

He put the photo down, picked up the glass and downed the amber-hued liquor. Sunny gasped as she saw him pick up the revolver.

"Oh, no!" she called out.

Seconds later, she landed, not gently, on Clint's front porch, just as the deafening sound of a gunshot shattered the mountain silence.

"Oh, no!" she cried again. She couldn't be too late! No longer concerned for her career, but desperate to save Clint Garvey's life, she burst through the door.

Clint glared at the hole he'd just put in his knotty pine plank wall. Hell, he couldn't even pull this off, he thought disgustedly. He'd pulled the barrel out of his mouth at the last instant, when it had suddenly dawned on him why his great-great-grandfather hadn't used this gun on himself more than a hundred years ago.

William must have believed that the woman he loved would not have wanted him to kill himself. And Clint had come to the same conclusion. Even though his mind was whiskey sodden, Clint knew that Laura would have been disappointed in him if he'd succeeded in pulling the trigger.

So, he thought, miserably, *now what?*

Before he could come up with an answer to that, his front door burst open and a strange woman rushed into the room.

"Oh, thank goodness, you didn't do it," she gasped, her hand at her throat. Her brown eyes were wide with distress, her face pale.

"Do what?"

"You know." She glanced nervously at the Colt revolver he was still holding in his hand. "Shoot yourself."

"What?" His laugh was harsh and bitter. "Look, lady, I don't know who the hell you are, or what you're doing in

my house, but for your information, I was cleaning my
great-great-grandfather's gun. And it went off."

She followed his gaze to the wall. "I see."

The bullet hole marring the gleaming wood filled Sunny
with renewed optimism. He hadn't truly wanted to kill
himself after all! At the last moment he'd found some reason to live. And that, she told herself, was enough to hang
her hopes on. Clint Garvey wasn't the lost cause she'd
feared.

"I'm glad one of us does," he muttered. He shook his
head and squinted at her. "How many of you are there?"

"Just one."

"I was afraid of that." He blinked, trying to get the dual
images to come together.

"I'm afraid you've had a bit too much to drink." Marc
Antony had also liked his wine, she recalled regretfully.
At least, Sunny thought, whatever Clint had been drinking could not have been nearly as lethal as the Hatfield's
moonshine.

"I'm afraid you're right." That said, Clint passed out.

"Well." Sunny stood with her hands on her hips looking down at the man slumped in his chair.

Clint Garvey was even more distressing in person than
he'd appeared on that oversize screen in her superior's office. His hair was long. Not trendy, male model long, but
shaggy and unkempt, hanging limply over the collar of his
rumpled denim shirt. From the stubble darkening his gaunt
cheeks, he obviously hadn't shaved for days. Which was
just as well, she decided, since if drinking to such excess
was routine behavior, he'd probably have cut his throat.

His eyes, now closed, had been tormented. And, she
thought, haunted.

"Talk about your challenges," she murmured. Obviously no woman in her right mind would want anything

to do with such a haggard, unkempt, humorless man. "You're a mess, Clint Garvey."

As was this house, she realized as her gaze swept over the stacks of unread newspapers piled beside the door, the dirty glasses scattered on tabletops, the layer of dust that had settled over everything like a shroud.

"But don't worry," she told the unconscious man, "you're in good hands."

She blinked twice. The first sent Clint out of the room. At the second blink, she followed.

He was now sprawled on his wide bed. Even as she admired the intricate hand carving on the headboard, Sunny was appalled at the state of his rumpled sheets. It had obviously been some time since they'd been washed.

"At least it appears you've been changing your underwear," she said as her appraising gaze took in the dirty clothes scattered over the plank flooring. "I suppose, at this point, I should be grateful for small favors."

Although she could have done it without moving a finger, something made Sunny bend down to pull off his boots as a mortal woman might. She considered undressing him, then decided to take advantage of his unconscious state to clean up his house. There was a great deal to be done. It would be better if she could at least set the stage for the challenge to come.

Sunny groaned as she walked into the kitchen and viewed even more unwashed glasses, coffee cups and dirty dishes piled in the sink. Fast-food containers filled the wastebasket and overflowed onto the floor. The refrigerator held beer and something green that looked as if it had once been a brick of cheese. The only thing she found in any of the cupboards was a half loaf of bread that had turned an even darker green than the cheese, and more bottles of whiskey.

Her task was to find Clint Garvey a wife. And part of her wanted to match the man passed out upstairs with the right woman because he desperately needed love. Another, equally strong part of her admitted to needing this match so she could keep her assignment in the romance division. But no woman would dare walk into this house for fear of catching the plague. Or worse.

"This is definitely going to be a challenge," she muttered as she wondered where to begin.

Some fairy godmothers might have been discouraged. But since such negative thoughts were against her nature, Sunny blinked to start the water running in the sink and reminded herself that not even Harmony had faced such a challenge. Which meant, she decided happily, as another blink created a thick layer of frothy white bubbles over the unwashed dishes, that if she pulled this off, she would definitely be in Harmony's lofty league.

THE FIRST THING Clint noticed, as he roused himself from his drunken stupor, was the tantalizing aroma wafting down the hall from the kitchen. If he hadn't known better, he would have thought it was beef stew. But of course that was impossible. Obviously, his mind was playing tricks on him again. The way it had when he'd thought there were blond women in his living room. Right after he'd shot a damn hole in his wall.

He pushed himself off the bed, and was not surprised when he couldn't remember how he'd gotten here. He'd been blacking out a lot lately. Rather than being upset by the missing hours, and sometimes days, Clint had come to appreciate the blackouts that kept him from remembering things too painful to think about.

He went into the adjoining bathroom and brushed his fuzzy teeth, then rinsed with mouthwash, assuring himself that if he was really flirting with alcoholism, as some of his friends had suggested, he would have swallowed the stuff.

Although he usually tried to avoid it, Clint made the mistake of looking into the mirror. He really did look like hell. Which exactly fit the way he felt.

The twinges of an impending headache began to stir behind his eyes. Having discovered that the most effective way to avoid a hangover was never to completely sober up, he left the bedroom, and headed toward the kitchen where he kept his liquor.

The rich aroma of beef cooking was even stronger out in the hall. "You're going freaking nuts," he told himself as he followed the wonderful scent. "Other drunks see bats when they get the d.t.'s. You smell stew." Which was, he reminded himself, a lot better than the scent of Laura's cologne he'd not been able to get out of his mind.

The shock hit his system the moment he entered his kitchen. His clean kitchen. Where the blond woman was standing at the stove. If this was a hallucination, it was definitely his weirdest one yet.

"What the hell?"

The woman turned, a wooden spoon in her hand. "Oh, you're awake," she said, greeting him with a warm smile as if there weren't anything unusual about her being in his kitchen.

"I hope you're hungry. I didn't know what you liked, but since you're a rancher, I thought that beef would be a safe bet. And, of course, stew is so nourishing, but if you'd rather—"

"Who the hell are you?" he demanded, entering the room on a long-legged, angry stride. "And what do you think you're doing in my house?"

She'd been right, Sunny thought as she was forced to tilt her head a long way back to look up at the man hovering over her. Clint Garvey was definitely tall.

"You don't remember?" Sunny had never enjoyed lying. However, since most people tended to disbelieve in the concept of fairy godmothers, she'd learned to hedge.

"If I remembered, I wouldn't have asked."

"True." She gave him her sweetest, most reassuring smile. "I came here earlier today. In answer to your ad."

"What ad? I didn't place any damn ad."

His low growl reminded her of a timber wolf. For a man who'd been unconscious only hours ago, he was definitely radiating an excess of dangerous energy.

"Of course you did." When forced to lie, Sunny did so blithely. "Let me get you a copy of the paper."

She went into the next room, and blinked. An oversize leather handbag appeared on the dining room table.

"I know it's in here somewhere," she assured him as she began digging through the handbag.

"It's not there because it doesn't exist."

"Of course it does."

Frustrated, and wishing she'd chosen a smaller bag, she dumped the contents out on the table and began digging through lipsticks, a compact, credit card receipts and . . . Tampax? Oh, dear. That's what she got for wishing for the contents of a normal mortal woman's purse.

Feeling the flush rising in her cheeks, she glanced over at the man who'd followed her into the dining room. But unlike her, he appeared unembarassed by the feminine product.

"You were saying?" he asked, arching a knowing brow that irritated her.

"It's here," she insisted as she continued to sort through the female paraphernalia. Heavens, she decided as she put aside a roll of masking tape and two packs of chewing gum, if this is what the average woman had to lug around, she was definitely grateful she wasn't mortal.

"Aha!" She held up the paper. "Eureka."

He took the piece of newsprint which appeared to have been torn from the *Rim Rock Record*'s classified advertising section.

"It's circled," she said helpfully. "In red ink." Personally, she thought that was a nice touch, especially for such a quick extemporaneous effort.

Clint still had a bit of a buzz on, but it didn't hamper his ability to focus on the ad in question. "'Wanted,'" he read out loud, "'housekeeper-cook. Five days a week. Room and board furnished, salary negotiable.'" And then, right there in black and white was his name. And directions to the ranch outside of Whiskey River.

He looked down at her. "There's been a mix-up. I didn't place this."

"It's your name," she said. As she leaned over to point it out to him, he caught a whiff of fresh spring rains and wildflowers. "And your address."

She had him there. "I didn't place it," he insisted.

Once again Sunny realized this was not going to be easy. She'd foolishly hoped that he'd be so pleased with his clean his house and home-cooked dinner, he'd beg her to stay on. So much for that plan.

Having always prided herself on her ability to improvise, she tried another tact.

"Oh dear." Sunny felt a bit guilty as her eyes filled with moisture, but she felt the situation called for drastic measures. "If you're telling the truth—"

"I don't have any reason to lie, dammit."

"Well, then." She twisted her hands together in front of her. "If you honestly didn't place the ad . . ." Her voice drifted off. In what she thought was a very nice touch, a tear trailed down her cheek. "I don't know what I'm going to do."

Reminding himself that he wasn't responsible for her dilemma, that this was either a mistake or a particularly clever con, Clint steeled himself against her tears.

"I'd suggest you go back to town. Or wherever it is you came from. And try the next ad on your list."

"But you were my only hope." Since this was absolutely true, it wasn't necessary for Sunny to fake the distress in her voice. "And I don't have any way to get back to town."

"How did you get all the way out here in the first place?"

"A nice man in a pickup gave me a ride." She figured that was safely vague enough.

He thought about giving her a lecture about the dangers of hitchhiking, then decided she wasn't any of his damn business. "All right. I'll drive you back into Whiskey River."

"You don't understand," she persisted. "I don't have anywhere else to go. And since you're obviously in desperate need of a housekeeper—"

"Look." His voice, sharp as a bullwhip, stung. "Get this straight. I don't need anyone."

"That's not true."

"Are you calling me a liar?" That was definitely the dumbest approach to winning a job he'd ever witnessed. But then again, Clint reminded himself, he wasn't interviewing her for any damn job.

"I'm saying that someone with your name who lives at this address has placed an ad for a housekeeper." She lifted her chin and met his challenging gaze straight on.

"And high time, too," she continued scathingly, "since I've never, in all my life, seen such a mess as your house was. And then, after I spent all day cleaning and scrubbing, not to mention fixing you a lovely dinner, you have the nerve to tell me that it's all some mistake?"

He appeared as unmoved by her irritation as he'd been her tears. "Where did you get the food?"

"What?"

"I asked where, exactly, did you get the food to cook this lovely dinner?"

Sunny wasn't at all pleased with the way he'd heaped an extra helping of scorn on the word lovely. Instead of pressuring her this way, he should be grateful she'd gone to the trouble. She was, after all, next to Hollyhock, the very best cook at Godmother Central.

"Oh. Why, at the market, of course."

"In Whiskey River."

"Yes."

"Want to tell me how you got there? Or did some other friendly man give you a ride all the way into town, then back out here again?"

For someone whose mind should have been dulled by drink, he was certainly being picky, Sunny thought. Still extemporizing, she said, "I brought some basics with me. You did say in the advertisement that you wanted someone who could cook."

He stared at her for a long time. "I still don't remember placing any damn ad."

She could hear the beginning hint of doubt in his voice and realized he was about to give in. At least on this. "I don't want to insult you," she said carefully, almost gently, "but it's obvious from all the empty bottles that I picked up, that you've been doing a bit of drinking lately."

"Gee, and here I thought no one would notice," he drawled.

He was not a pleasant man. Even after she got him cleaned up, Sunny feared it would not be easy to find him a wife. If she didn't possess such a trusting nature, she might have suspected she'd been given this assignment in the hope that she'd wash out of the romance program.

Determined that that not happen, she decided to try reason. "Obviously there's been some sort of mix-up."

"That's what I've been trying to tell you."

"Yes. Well . . . Why don't we discuss our little problem over dinner?"

As he opened his mouth to tell her that the only one with the problem around here was her, she went back over to the pot and lifted the lid, allowing a mouthwatering steam to escape. Then she took a loaf of fresh-baked, golden-topped bread from the oven.

Hell. He could resist her apparent distress about not getting a job that didn't exist. He could turn his back on her sweet scent. He wondered for only a second if those wild, springy blond curls were as soft as they looked, and was able to tamp down the hunger stirred by the sight of her bending over the oven door in her short plaid skirt.

Unfortunately, the first real food he'd seen—or smelled—in weeks was irresistible.

"I'm not going to change my mind," he warned, suspecting a snare the way a wolf senses a trap buried in the forest.

"That's certainly your prerogative." She began spooning the stew into deep bowls he hadn't seen for days. Not since he'd run out of cornflakes.

"But I will pay you for the work you've already done." That was only fair, he decided, wondering how she could have made such inroads into the mess his house had been in such a short amount of time.

She threw him a dazzling smile over her shoulder. "That's very kind of you. Why don't we discuss it after dinner?"

"Fine." He knew what she was doing and wasn't going to let it happen. He opened the refrigerator, found it stocked with food that hadn't been there earlier, and pulled out a beer. "We'll settle it while I drive you back to Whiskey River."

"Whatever you'd like," she agreed without missing a beat.

It wasn't really a lie, Sunny assured herself. Well, perhaps it was a little white one. But since it was for his own good, she conveniently decided that it didn't count.

2

HUMMING SOFTLY BENEATH her breath, Sunny cut several thick slices of bread with a serrated knife, then liberally spread one of them with creamy yellow butter. As he watched it melt, Clint could feel his mouth watering.

She put the bowls and basket of bread on the table she'd set earlier. From the way he'd been staring at the food, she expected he'd immediately sit down and begin wolfing it down. Instead he stunned her by pulling out her chair.

They ate in silence for a time. Clint's attention was directed solely on his food, while Sunny watched him surreptitiously from beneath lowered lashes as she ate her dinner.

"You're not a bad cook," he said after a while.

"Thank you." She smiled across the table at him, wondering what he'd say if she'd told him that she'd once cooked dinner for Julius Caesar.

"Where did you get the flowers?"

She'd put the arrangement of red and white carnations and holly in the center of the table after cleaning off what appeared to be months of newspapers.

"I found them in the grocery store. I thought they'd add a little holiday spirit."

"Holiday?"

"You know. Christmas?"

"Oh, yeah."

His disinterest was easy to understand, she thought. Obviously, he wouldn't be looking forward to a season that celebrated the family and the hope a baby brought into the world.

"I can take them away," she offered. "If you don't like them."

"I don't care one way or the other. But I suppose you'll expect me to reimburse you for them, too."

The temper that Sunny had not known she possessed flared again. "Do you know," she said, pointing her spoon at him, "it's one thing to suffer a loss. I can understand how you might not feel like being overly cheerful after the year you've had. However, that is no excuse for ill manners."

His eyes narrowed, and pinned her with a cold deadly look. "What the hell do you know about the year I've had?"

"Well, it isn't exactly a secret," she replied. Actually, from what she'd read of the case in the file that had magically appeared on the table beside her conjured-up bag, the death of Clint's married lover—whose husband had been reported to be the Republicans' great hope to regain the White House—had made headlines all over the world.

"Anyone ever tell you that you're a master of understatement?" he asked dryly. He'd been reaching for his beer, but instead, his hand curled into a fist on the top of the table. "Hell, they probably know about Laura's murder on Mars."

He flinched as he said his sweetheart's name, and Sunny's irritation was replaced by compassion. Allowing her heart to rule her head, as she so often did, she reached across the table and covered his fisted hand with hers.

"I'm sorry."

"You didn't kill her," he muttered.

"No. But I wish I could bring her back for you."

He laughed at that, but the cold wintry sound chilled her blood. "You and me both, baby."

It was not often Sunny was allowed a sojourn on earth, and usually one of the things she looked forward to most on such occasions was the amazing variety of food she was able to prepare and enjoy. But a dismal mood had settled over the room, like a depressing, wet gray fog. The stew suddenly lost its appeal and the bread, which earlier had possessed a wonderfully yeasty flavor now tasted like ashes in her mouth.

It did not escape her attention that Clint, too, seemed to have lost his appetite. He polished off the beer, went over to the refrigerator for another, then seemed to reconsider. He shut the door and instead pulled down a new bottle of whiskey from the cupboard next to the stove.

"I'm not certain you should do that," she said quietly.

"What did you say your name was?" he snapped. "Jiminy Cricket?"

"It's Sunny," she said, ignoring that conscious crack. "And I was only suggesting that if you intend to drive me back down that twisting road to town, perhaps you should refrain from drinking any more alcohol." She had no intention of leaving, of course, but that wasn't the point at the moment.

"Now you sound like a public service commercial." He tore the seal and unscrewed the cap. "Friends don't let friends drive drunk, isn't that how it goes?"

Although there was a rack of glasses beside him, he ignored them and took a long swig directly from the bottle. While he swallowed, he kept his eyes on hers in what Sunny understood to be a challenge.

"Actually, I'm amazed you have any friends left," she murmured.

The whiskey burned in a soothing, familiar sort of way. Soon, with any luck, not only would he not be able to drive, he wouldn't be able to think. To remember.

"My friends, or lack of them, aren't any of your business."

"True. But although I've been called reckless in my time, I'm not stupid enough to get into a truck with a man who's been drinking."

Unfortunately, she had a point. He had enough guilt on his conscience as it was. There was no way he wanted to risk killing this woman whose only crime had been to clean his house, cook him the best meal he'd had in months, hell, perhaps ever, and still somehow manage to be a royal pain in the ass.

"I'll make you a deal."

"What?" She folded her arms across the front of her scarlet sweater embroidered with a trio of black scotties wearing plaid hair bows that matched her short skirt. The motion drew his attention to her breasts which, although not voluptuous, filled the sweater out nicely.

"I'll drink however much I want. But I'll give you the keys to the truck and you can drive yourself back to town."

"Then how will you get it back again?"

He shrugged. "Don't worry about that. I'll figure out a way."

"When you're sober."

He heard the censure in her tone and didn't like it. "Yeah." He took another swig. "When I'm sober."

Becoming more frustrated by the moment, Sunny decided that if Clint Garvey kept behaving like a bratty two-year-old, she was going to forget she'd ever felt sorry for him. "And when do you think that will be?" she asked. "Sometime in the next millennium?"

His laugh was short and mirthless. "Anyone ever tell you that you've got a smart mouth?"

"Anyone ever tell you that you're not the first person to lose someone you love?"

The accusation, which had flown off the tip of her tongue in frustration, scored a direct hit. She watched as a cold shadow moved over his crystal blue eyes and a muscle began to twitch in his cheek.

"Bull's-eye," he murmured.

They stood, a few feet apart, staring at each other. Sunny wished she could take the incautious words back. She sighed, feeling sorry that she'd wounded him, and guilty that she was more concerned that he'd send her away, blowing her chance to remain in the romance ranks.

"I'm sorry," she murmured. "I had no right to say that."

He shrugged. "You don't have to apologize for speaking your mind. And you're right. I'm not the first man to lose the woman he loved. And I won't be the last."

"No. But that doesn't make it hurt any less."

"It's not going to work," he growled, the brief truce suddenly broken again.

"What?"

Yeah, that nagging little voice in the back of his mind echoed, what the hell are you complaining about? Do you have a problem with the idea that a kind, seemingly generous, beautiful woman might actually give a damn whether or not you live or die? Clint ignored the faint voice of reason. As he had for months.

"The sweetness-and-light routine," he said gruffly. "You could be freaking Mary Poppins and I still wouldn't be in the market for a housekeeper." He took another long drink, feeling a bit like a rebellious adolescent daring his parents to ground him for bad behavior.

Sunny understood his defiance and refused to play along. While she was trying to figure out her next move, he dug into the pocket of his jeans and pulled out a roll of money which he held out to her.

"Is this enough?" He cursed when he received a blank look in response. "For the damn groceries. And your work."

She didn't count it, but since there was a hundred dollar bill on top, she suspected it was more than generous. "Yes, but—"

"Then that's it."

Clint was not normally rude, although admittedly even before Laura's murder he wouldn't have won any contests for Whiskey River's Mr. Congeniality. But there was something about this woman—an indefinable something that disturbed him more than he cared to admit.

Determined to get her out of his house, he dug down into the pocket again, and pulled out a set of keys. "Here. The truck's parked in the driveway. It's all yours."

"How do you know I won't just keep the truck?"

"What makes you think I give a damn?" He reached out, grabbed her hand, stuck the keys in it, then closed her fingers. "Go away, whatever your name is—"

"Sunny," she reminded him in a voice that was almost a whisper.

"Wouldn't you know it?" His mouth twisted in a parody of a smile. "Go away, Sunny. There's nothing for you here." Before she could argue further, he put his arm around her shoulder and practically pushed her out the kitchen door.

"I can't drive a truck."

"Don't worry. It's an automatic. All you have to do is put it in drive and steer."

So much for that ploy. Having no other choice, Sunny blinked and in her mind's eye watched the far side rear tire go flat.

"Is there something wrong with that tire?" she asked innocently.

The mercury-vapor light on the side of the nearby garage cast a wide yellow glow that illuminated the tire she'd flattened. He followed her gaze and cursed ripely.

"Wait here. I'll get the spare."

That's what he thought. Another blink caused an entire string of curses.

"What's the matter?"

"The spare's flat, too."

"Oh, dear."

Even through the comforting alcohol fog that was beginning to settle over his brain once again, Clint thought he detected an insincere note in her calm tone.

He pulled a pack of cigarettes out of his shirt, lit one, and puffed thoughtfully as he submitted her to a long look. Her expression was one of absolute innocence. But there was something not quite right, something he couldn't put his finger on that kept him from trusting her.

"You realize of course, that there's no way you're going to get down the mountain tonight."

"You don't have another spare?"

"No. I'll have to fix this one in the morning."

"I'm sorry if I'm being an inconvenience."

Clint knew, with every fiber of his being, that she was not sorry. However, he decided there was no point in calling her a liar: he'd simply let her spend the night, then send her the hell on her way in the morning.

He cursed again. Then he turned and strode back toward the house. Trying to keep the smile of satisfaction off her face, Sunny followed him back into the kitchen.

"I don't suppose you happened to bring some clothes with you when you came to apply for that job that doesn't exist."

"Actually, I did."

He shook his head. "Why doesn't that surprise me? The bathroom's at the top of the stairs. The spare bedroom is the first door on the left."

"Thank you—"

"Just don't get too comfortable," he snarled, "because you'll be leaving in the morning."

"I've always heard about western hospitality," Sunny said as she felt her temper beginning to simmer again, "but it's so illuminating to see it in action."

"I never invited you here in the first place," he reminded her. "So technically, you're not a guest."

"Point taken." She eyed the bottle he'd picked up again. "Why don't I make some coffee before I do the dishes?" she suggested.

"I don't want any damn coffee. As for the dishes, leave them."

"But—"

"Look, lady—"

"Sunny," she reminded him helpfully.

"Look, Sunny, the dinner was great. Better than great. It was world-class. And you seem to be a very nice woman. You're also kind of cute, and, as a bonus, you smell real good, too. In fact I'm sure, under other circumstances, you'd be real dandy company.

"But you have to understand that I've had about all the conversation I can handle for one night. And right now, if you don't mind, I'd just like to be left alone."

Deciding that having won the evening skirmish, she could tackle the war in the morning, Sunny decided to do as he asked.

"Of course," she agreed mildly.

Clint followed her into the living room, where she retrieved the overnight bag he could have sworn hadn't been there when he'd come through the room on the way to the kitchen earlier.

Of course it had been there, he told himself later, as he put the remainder of the stew into the refrigerator. Did he think that she'd conjured it up out of thin air?

Deciding he was definitely losing it, Clint went into the living room, where he sat in the dark, with only his new best friend Jim Beam for company, and proceeded to get quietly and desperately drunk.

IN THE MORNING it was the smell of coffee that woke him. Dark and rich and alluring, it teased at his senses, offering blessed relief for the headache that was pounding behind his eyes. At first Clint thought he must be dreaming. Then, as he heard the clatter of pots and pans coming from the kitchen, he remembered the woman who'd shown up yesterday in answer to that ad he'd never placed in the *Rim Rock Record*.

As he had the night before, he followed the aroma and discovered her standing in front of the open refrigerator door. Today's outfit was a Christmas red sweater and pair of matching leggings that accentuated her legs, which were, he admitted reluctantly, damn good. Her hair, tumbling down her back nearly to her waist, was a riot of untamed curls that glistened like gold dust in the morning sunlight streaming through the window.

"That coffee smells good," he said.

His voice obviously startled her; she jumped and dropped the eggs she'd just taken from the cardboard container. "Oh, no!"

Sunny watched in dismay as the eggs broke, turning into a sticky goo on the clean floor. She was about to blink and clean up the mess when she realized that Clint was watching.

She turned on him, her heart still pounding wildly. "You scared me to death, sneaking up on me like that!"

Her eyes were wide and startled, reminding Clint of a skittish doe caught in his truck headlights. "Sorry. I guess I should ask permission before coming into my own kitchen."

His tone, laced with its usual sarcasm, only irritated her further. "I see you aren't any more pleasant in the morning than you are at night."

"Then you should be happy that you're leaving this morning."

"I've had easier assignments," she muttered, glaring down at the mess at her feet. Since he didn't look as if he were going to leave the room any time soon, she realized she was actually going to have to clean the sticky stuff up the mortal way. By hand.

Muttering a low curse beneath her breath, she yanked a handful of paper towels from the wooden holder, knelt down and began sponging.

Clint watched her for a moment, told himself that the gentlemanly thing to do would be to help her out, then decided that if he encouraged her even the slightest bit, she might try to talk him into letting her stay on. Which was, of course, out of the question.

He stepped over the broken eggs, took a mug down from the rack, poured a cup of the coffee and took a tentative sip. It was black as midnight and strong, just the way he liked it.

"This isn't bad," he said.

She was about to snap back that she was ever so pleased he approved when she realized that his tone had been almost friendly. She glanced a long, long way up, looking for some sense of what he was thinking. But his expression was as unreadable as ever and if the eyes were indeed windows to the man's soul, he'd pulled down the shades to keep anyone from getting a glimpse.

"Thank you."

"You're welcome."

She continued to look up at him in the hope he'd say something else. Anything else. Such as since she made the best coffee he'd ever tasted, perhaps she'd like to stay on and make it for him every morning.

His beard was heavier this morning, creating a dark shadow on his haggard cheeks that echoed the dark, purplish blue shadows beneath his eyes. His hair looked as if it had been combed by thrusting his fingers through it and he was wearing the same clothes he'd had on last night. Obviously, he'd gotten drunk again after she'd left him alone.

"I thought I'd fix waffles this morning," she said, bestowing her cheeriest smile on him. Even the obstreperous mountain man, Devil Anse Hatfield, had not been able to resist its charm. "Unless you'd rather have hotcakes."

An image flashed through his mind—an image of the last morning he and Laura had spent together. He'd come downstairs after his shower to find her standing at the stove, wearing a frilly apron—and nothing else—flipping hotcakes. The smile she'd flashed over her shoulder had been even more provocative than her outfit and he'd taken her, right on the biscuit-hued kitchen counter with a passion that had left them both breathless.

Later, when the blare of the smoke alarm and the billowing gray clouds rising from the pan revealed the pancakes had burned to charcoal, they'd both laughed.

"Oh well," Laura had said pragmatically, as she'd dumped the charred breakfast into the garbage disposal, "after tonight we'll have lots more chances to have breakfast together."

"A lifetime," he'd agreed as he'd kissed her sweet, smiling lips.

The following morning she was gone. Her life cut tragically short.

The memory caused ragged claws of pain and regret to rip at his insides. "I'd rather you just stop trying to be frigging Donna Reed," he growled.

He swallowed the coffee in long gulps, and then, although he desperately needed a drink to dull the ache, he reminded himself that the goal at the moment was to get this sweet smelling interloper out of his house. And his life. That being the case, he'd have to stay sober enough to drive her into town. Then, once she was gone, he could lose himself in the bottle.

After the way he'd wolfed down last night's stew, Sunny had hoped that the way to Clint Garvey's heart might be through his stomach. Unfortunately, that didn't seem to be the case.

She sighed as he left the kitchen, slamming the door behind him. She had not a single doubt that he'd have the spare tire fixed within minutes. And since he was sober, she couldn't even refuse to drive to Whiskey River with him.

Looking down at the gooey mess she'd made, she wondered how mortal women managed to keep a household running without magic. She blinked and was relieved when it disappeared. Then she stood up and went over to the window, and watched as Clint took the flat tire off the truck.

The sky overhead was a bright blue bowl, forecasting a clear day. Sunny lifted her hand and made a wide, swirling gesture. Dark clouds suddenly appeared on the horizon, and the red mercury line on the thermometer outside the window dropped dramatically as the swirling clouds swept toward Whiskey River. Moments later, the first blizzard of the season had begun.

3

"WHAT THE HELL?" Clint looked up in surprise as he was suddenly hit in the face by wind-driven snow. He might not be as coherent lately as he'd once been, but he knew damn well that the sun had been shining when he'd come out here.

Now it was snowing so hard he could barely see the house only a few yards away. And it felt like the freaking North Pole. Having lived in Arizona's high country all his life, Clint was accustomed to unpredictable weather. But he'd never witnessed such a rapid drop in temperature; not even during the summer monsoon season when thunderstorms tended to hit the rim like speeding freight trains.

He'd barely gotten the third lug nut off when his fingers felt as if they were about to turn to ice. Cursing ripely, he surrendered the battle and marched back toward the house. Any storm that hit this fast would be on its way to Albuquerque within the hour. Then he could come back outside, finish repairing the tire, and get rid of little Miss Sunshine, or whatever her name was.

She was setting the pine trestle kitchen table when he walked in the door. "I thought I'd serve breakfast in here," she said, behaving as if he hadn't already told her he didn't want anything. "Unless you'd rather eat in the dining room—"

"You don't get it, do you?"

"Get what?"

"I don't want to eat in the kitchen. Or the dining room. I don't want breakfast, I don't want a housekeeper, and I definitely don't want some clumsy scatterbrained blonde hanging around my house. Even if she can make a decent cup of coffee."

"And stew," she reminded him. "With dumplings."

Was she deaf? Or screwed up in the head? He remembered a kid in high school, who'd gotten kicked in the head by a horse he'd been trying to ride in the saddle bronc competition of the Junior Rodeo national finals. Although he'd survived, Billy Young had never been the same again. Talking to him had been like talking to a wall, Clint remembered.

"You ever ride a horse?"

"No, although I've always wanted to. They seem like such wonderful animals. Why?"

He shrugged. "You just remind me of someone I used to know."

"Oh." Sunny gave him another of those winsome smiles. "The waffles are already made," she coaxed. "Would it hurt you to eat them? It seems like such a waste to throw them out."

Another thing growing up in ranching country had taught him, along with expecting erratic weather, was to be frugal. Since the cow business wasn't all that lucrative—at least it never had been for the Garveys—Clint had learned at an early age never to throw anything away. Most things could be repaired or remade into something else. Or you just did without. Her words struck a responsive chord.

"Wouldn't want to be accused of letting good food go to waste," he muttered as he went over to the sink to wash his hands. After he rinsed off the lather, he turned, intending to tear a paper towel from the roll and found her standing beside him, holding out a cotton dish towel.

"How did you do that?"

"Do what?"

"A second ago you were over by the stove. Now you're here."

"A second ago you were by the door. And now you're here," she returned.

Good point. But he remembered walking across the room. For the life of him, he couldn't remember seeing her move.

"It's hard to concentrate with a headache," she commiserated. She put a hand on his arm. "Why don't you sit down and I'll pour you a refill."

Her hand looked as smooth as porcelain; her fingers were long and slender, her nails unpainted. For a fleeting second, Clint imagined how that hand might feel on his body, which had gone so many months without a woman's touch. Then, feeling guilty for being unfaithful to Laura—albeit only in his thoughts—he firmly closed his mind to the unbidden notion.

Not wanting to let her insinuate herself further into his life, yet unable to resist her offer of more coffee, Clint moved away from her light touch and sat down at the table. Although her expression remained polite, he thought he caught just the faintest glimpse of triumph in her gaze.

She placed the stack of waffles in front of him.

"Aren't you going to have anything?" he asked when she remained standing beside him.

"Oh, I don't really think that's a very good idea."

"Why not?"

"Well, you're the employer. And I'm just the house-keeper."

"You're not the housekeeper. You're not going to *be* the housekeeper. And I'd rather have you sitting across the table than hovering over me while I'm trying to eat."

"I wasn't hovering over you."

"Of course you were. Now get a plate and sit down."

It was an order. Softly couched, but carved in stone. Sunny saw no point in arguing.

She took a plate down from the shelf, a knife and fork from the drawer and sat down at the table across from him.

"That's better." He stabbed a whole wheat waffle and deposited it on her plate. Then he drenched his own in maple syrup and took a bite. "It's pretty good," he said, torn between the need to compliment her and the reluctance to encourage her.

"Thank you. Of course, if the contents of your refrigerator and pantry were any indication, it's been a while since you had any home cooking. Good or bad."

"Got me there," he said agreeably.

Clint kind of liked the way she talked back to him. She wasn't as easily intimidated as many of the fine citizens of Whiskey River. Although he'd always been pretty much of a loner in the western ranching community, ever since Laura's murder—even though he'd been proven innocent and released from jail—there were still people who crossed the street when they saw him coming. And the few friends he did have in town had been tiptoeing around him as if they were afraid of saying anything that might depress him.

As if his life weren't already as damn depressing as it could get.

"It looks as if we're in for quite a storm," Sunny said, glancing out the window where the driven snow had reduced the visibility to nearly zero.

Clint glared out at the white stuff being whipped against the glass. "It'll pass," he muttered. "It always does."

Sunny didn't argue with that. Nor did she agree. But Clint found the faint smile hovering at the corners of her full rosy lips suspicious, just the same.

As he and Sunny had done last night, they finished the meal in silence. When he leaned back and lit a cigarette, Sunny took it as a sign he was done and began clearing the table.

"I haven't figured out why yet, but for some reason you're determined to worm your way into my life, aren't you?"

His tone and his description irked Sunny. "You've such a way with words. And why would your life, which you seemed willing to throw away, be any of my business?"

"Good question. Are you saying I'm mistaken?"

"No."

"Aha." He nodded, satisfied.

"I'm saying you're dead wrong." It was, admittedly, an out-and-out lie. But she didn't believe he was ready for the truth.

"All right." He blew out a plume of smoke. "Let me re-phrase it, then. How about, you're determined to worm your way into my house?"

"That isn't much better. But it's closer." She met his steady, challenging gaze. "I told you last night," she said softly, "I don't have anywhere else to go."

"You don't have any family?"

"No."

"No husband, kids?"

"No." She did not add that that was one of the few downsides to her career as a fairy godmother.

"How about lovers?"

The way he was suddenly looking at her, as if seeing her as a woman for the first time, made Sunny suddenly very nervous. Her skin warmed beneath the unwavering gaze and although she was certain it must be her imagination, it seemed the pulse in the base of her throat had suddenly trebled its beat.

"No." She tried to drag her eyes from his and found herself inescapably snared by that appraising blue gaze.

"No?" He shook his head. "Baby, the guys must all be dead from the waist down where you come from."

It was not a compliment. Not really. But Sunny's mutinous body strangely decided to take it as one. "I wouldn't know about that," she murmured. "Would you like some more coffee?"

He ignored her offer. "What would you do," he asked instead, "if I told you that you could have the job?"

"Really?" Pleasure lit her eyes to a burnished gold that made him almost feel guilty about what he was about to say. "Do you mean it?"

"I never say anything I don't mean." He rubbed his chin and continued to smoke as he gave her a deliberately slow perusal from the top of her gilt head down to her feet, clad in a pair of high-top sneakers with scarlet laces. "Ask anyone."

His gaze returned to her face which was still flushed with pleasure. He wondered idly how pleased she'd be when she heard the rest of his offer.

"You already know about Laura."

"Yes." She nodded. The sympathetic shadow in her gleaming eyes created another little prick of guilt that Clint steadfastly ignored. "You must have loved her a great deal."

"I did. Absolutely. Unequivocally." He took another long drag on the cigarette. "Needless to say, I haven't been up to rejoining the dating game these past few months."

"Oh, I can understand that." She rushed over, sat down in the chair beside him and took his free hand in hers. "It's not easy, getting back into the swing of things."

Pleased with how this conversation seemed to have taken an unexpectedly romantic turn, Sunny was tempted to explain her presence here in Whiskey River. What a relief it would be for Clint to learn he wasn't going to have to go searching for a new love because it was her job to find one for him!

He looked down at their linked fingers—his dark, hers as pale as the snow that was falling outside—and felt a strange pull that wasn't quite sexual, but disturbing just the same.

"The thing is," he continued, ignoring this new feeling as he'd ignored the guilt, "celibacy can get a little monotonous, if you know what I mean. So, although I've never stooped to paying a woman, I suppose I could make an exception." He paused, watching for his words to sink in. "In your case."

"I don't understand." She spoke slowly, her wide, innocent eyes on his. "Are you actually offering to pay me to make love with you?"

"No."

"Oh." The single word was expelled on a long breath. Her relief was so palpable, Clint felt as if he could reach out and touch it.

"This doesn't have anything to do with love. I'm talking about sex. Since you need a place to stay, and I'll admit to getting damn horny, it seems the logical thing for us to do is work out a deal that solves both our problems."

Sunny was not an absolute innocent. Several centuries of observing the inhabitants of the world had allowed her to witness everything—good and evil—that human beings did to, and with, one another. She should not have been shocked when Clint took her for a prostitute, but she was both shocked and hurt.

"I can't believe you said that."

She looked so distressed and her voice was trembling so that Cliff, who'd decided the ad was a ruse, almost apologized. She was such a damn good actress, he was sure that Mariah had to be at the bottom of this deception. Even though Laura's younger sister had left Hollywood after inheriting the Swann ranch, she still wrote screenplays and the occasional made-for-television movie. She'd know lots of would-be starlets who'd be willing to go to bed for a part. Or even the rent money.

He was a little disappointed that Mariah, who knew better than anyone how much he'd loved Laura, would think that a warm female body in his bed would make up for all he'd lost. But then again, she'd lived in Tinseltown for a long time; maybe among the lotus eaters, sex wasn't taken so seriously.

"It was Mariah, wasn't it?" he asked, deciding to get the game playing over with.

"Mariah?" Sunny asked blankly.

"She's the one who hired you. She's the one who sent you here."

"I told you, I came because of that ad—"

"Yeah, the one in the *Rim Rock Record*." That brought up another possibility. "Which means Mac had to be in on the scheme, too."

"Mac?"

"Mackenzie Reardon. He's publisher of the paper." He was also an old friend. "He's getting married to Noel Giraudeau."

"Princess Noel Giraudeau?"

The stunning blonde, the papparazzi had dubbed the Ice Princess had once gone on a photo safari with the Princess of Wales. Sunny remembered the occasion all too well because when the Prince of Wales had opted out of the trip at the last minute, Sunny had harbored doubts about his commitment to what she'd hoped was a true love match. With the crystal clear view of hindsight, Sunny realized she should have given up on the relationship right then.

"Yeah."

"From what I've seen—in the papers—" Sunny said quickly, when his eyes narrowed again, "the princess seems to be a lovely woman."

"Inside and out," Clint confirmed, his expression softening slightly at the mention of the woman who'd expressed such concern for him over these past months. "And since I don't think she'd agree to the scheme, Mariah and Mac must have done it on their own." He was also certain that Mariah's new husband, Trace Callahan, would not have had anything to do with such an illegal arrangement. Although he admittedly hadn't been thinking all that clearly in those days immediately following Laura's death, the one thing that had sunk in was that Whiskey River's sheriff definitely took his job seriously.

"I'm not a prostitute." She lifted her chin. "And I definitely didn't come here to have sex with you."

He gave her another long look. Just when Sunny's nerves were approaching the screaming point, he shrugged.

"Too bad."

Before she could come up with a response to that, he stood up, pulled his shearling-lined jacket from a hook on the wall and shrugged into it.

"Where are you going?"

He threw her a look over his shoulder. "I figured I'd go out and feed the horses. Unless you've changed your mind about the sex?"

"No." She bit her lip to keep from asking him to please be patient. Just a little longer.

As he watched her small white teeth worrying that soft pink flesh, Clint felt the age-old attraction of male for female, and decided it was definitely time to leave.

"Too bad," he repeated, then left the cozy warmth of the kitchen.

As she watched him disappearing into the swirling white snow, Sunny closed her eyes, and wished, for a fleeting moment, that she was a mortal woman. One who could take him to his bed and soothe the pain that never left his haunted eyes. A ragged pain she feared he could feel all the way to his soul.

Minutes passed. Although she was admittedly a little out of practice when it came to computing earth time when the grandfather clock in the front room tolled the hour on a pleasing peal of Westminster chimes, Sunny was sure Clint had been outside far too long.

Standing at the window, she shut out the blizzard and tried desperately to focus on him. To hear him, or see him. But there was nothing. Only a deep black void behind her lids that changed to a blurry white world when she opened her eyes.

"What's wrong?" she wondered out loud. She glanced up, half expecting an answer, disappointed when none was forthcoming. "Why can't I see him?"

A thought occurred to her, more chilling than the weather. What if he'd done what he'd been about to do when she'd first arrived? What if he'd killed himself? Or even worse, what if he'd shot himself, but was still alive, barely clinging to existence, his life force slowly draining away, so weak she was unable to sense it?

Making romantic matches that failed was a bad enough stain on her permanent record. There was no way Sunny was going to allow an assignment to die. And even as she ran out into the snow in search of him, she knew that her need to find Clint, to save him, went a great deal deeper than mere duty.

The icy wind whipped away his name as soon as it escaped her lips. Unaccustomed to mortal form, she'd forgotten about the need for any kind of overcoat, and desperately tried to recall the temperature at which human blood froze.

She conjured up a vision of a jacket, the twin of Clint's shearling-lined one, blinked, and was both surprised and troubled when she didn't immediately find herself wrapped in its warmth. She blinked again. Nothing.

Distressed and confused, she waved her ice-cold hand in a graceful arc, deciding that her only hope was to stop the blizzard. But the snow continued to drift down like feathers shaken from a huge down pillow overhead and the temperature continued to drop.

As much as she longed for the safety and warmth of the house, Sunny was even more concerned about Clint's safety. Her feet felt like blocks of ice and as she made her way through the drifting white snow, hopefully in the direction he'd taken, she found it more and more difficult to keep her legs moving.

She fell once, stumbling to her knees in a deep drift. She pushed herself to her feet and kept on going. After stum-

bling a second time, it was even more difficult to stand up.
But she made it. Only to fall a third time.

"Damn you, Clint Garvey," she muttered on something between a sob and a wail, "I've never, in all my life,
been given such an impossible assignment."

She wasn't going to fail, Sunny assured herself as she
struggled to her feet yet again and continued trudging forward. Now the wind was blowing ice in her face that stung
like needles against her cheeks. She began to wonder if
she'd gone the wrong way. Surely the barn wasn't this far
from the house?

She looked around her, but saw nothing but a white
curtain in all directions. She made a cone with her hands
again and called out his name. But as before, the only answer was the howl of the wind in the tops of the white-
frosted pine trees.

Disoriented, she tried to remember the direction she'd
seen him take when he'd left the kitchen, but she was exhausted from the cold and effort and discouragement.

She cried out as she stumbled over a downed tree that
had been buried by the snow. Snow she'd thought she'd
been oh, so clever in stirring up in the first place. She was
on her hands and knees when she realized she had no
strength to go another foot. She sank back into the snowbank, feeling more alone than she'd ever felt in her life.

SUNNY WAS FAR from alone. Two fairy godmothers—one
tall and spare, the other short and pleasingly plump—
watched her desperate struggles.

"Are you certain this is the thing to do?" Andromeda
asked. "It's been a very long time since the girl has visited
earth. She's obviously forgotten mortal survival skills."

"She won't need them," Harmony said with her usual
unwavering confidence.

"But perhaps we could slow the storm—"

"No." The smile gracing the face of the legendary fairy godmother was almost beatific. "Sunny was the one who conjured up the storm. She was the one who asked to be mortal. She'll have to learn to live with the consequences."

"Then she will live?"

"Of course. I have very special plans for our Sunny. Plans that will solve both our problems."

Harmony's smile widened and her eyes danced merrily. It had been a long time since she'd experienced the joys of a seemingly impossible assignment. She'd always believed in going out while you were on top, which was why she'd retired after the prince had taken sweet, pretty, admittedly dim little Cindy to his palace, where they had gone on to live happily ever after.

Clint Garvey was definitely no prince. At least not the chivalrous knight-in-shining-armor type that filled the gilt-edged pages of fairy-tale books. But Harmony knew him to be a special man, imbued with a steely integrity and capable of a deep and abiding love, even if he believed he had no more love to give.

The trick was to find him an equally special woman— a brave, intelligent resourceful woman. One spirited enough to stand up to him and patient enough to prove to him that he was better than he thought he was.

Who better than Sunny to tempt and torment him, even as she taught him to trust again?

"I still wonder if we should have told her the truth," Andromeda continued to fret.

Such worry was uncharacteristic, but Sunny was a special case. Although she tried not to become emotionally attached to the students who were assigned to her for a brief time before moving up in the hierarchy, it had been impossible not to grow fond of the always optimistic, open-hearted young apprentice fairy godmother.

"It's better this way."

"But what if the girl actually manages to make a match? What if she matches Clint Garvey with the wrong woman? She does have a disastrous history of doing just that."

"Ah, but she isn't the one making this match," Harmony reminded her long-time friend. "I am."

That said, she waved her wand and watched with satisfaction as the magic dust made the falling snow suddenly begin to sparkle like diamonds as it settled over Sunny.

4

CLINT WAS ON his way back to the house when he nearly stumbled over Sunny. "What the hell are you doing out here?" he demanded as he scooped her out of the snowbank.

"I was trying to rescue you," she said without an instant's hesitation.

Clint cursed inwardly. "Who do you think you are, lady? My guardian angel?"

Sunny latched on to his words, not noticing that they'd been ground out through clenched teeth. Relieved that he was the one to have brought the subject up, Sunny impulsively decided to tell him the truth. If Clint Garvey could accept the fact that she had only his best interests at heart, he'd undoubtedly be more willing to accept the woman she chose for him.

As they entered the house, she smiled her warmest, most beguiling smile. A smile designed to assure him that he was in good hands. "Actually, since you brought it up, that's close. Actually, I'm your fairy godmother."

Hell, she was either nuts, or being out in that blizzard had frozen some brain cells.

"How stupid of me not to have recognized you right off the bat," he drawled, as he plunked her down on a kitchen chair. "I suppose my only excuse is that I mistook you for Glinda the Good Witch."

Sunny's spirits sagged. The warmth she'd begun to feel in her veins upon entering the room faded. "You don't believe me."

"What's not to believe? Doesn't everyone have a fairy godmother?" The sarcasm in his voice echoed that in his icy blue eyes.

"Of course they do, but—"

"So where are your gilded wings?"

Although she knew his question was meant to be rhetorical, she decided to answer it anyway. "Now you're referring to guardian angels. I'm a fairy—"

"Godmother. Yeah, we've already established that. So, what happens now? Do I get three wishes?"

"That's a genie."

"Boy, you guys are really specialized, aren't you? Next thing you'll be telling me that you've gotten together and formed unions, like the Teamsters and the Screenwriters Guild."

"It's understandable that you'd have difficulty accepting the idea. But there's no reason to be nasty."

Clint's head was still pounding from all the whiskey he'd drunk the evening before. He was the closest thing to sober he'd been in weeks and he wasn't enjoying the way it felt. Still, he admitted, just because he was suffering the mother of all hangovers was no reason to take his filthy mood out on her.

"You're right. And I apologize."

The thing to do, he decided, was to warm her up, wait out the storm, then get her out of his house—and his life—as soon as possible. The more he allowed himself to be drawn into conversation with her, the more he'd be in danger of her dragging him back into the world of the living. The world that just yesterday he'd wanted to leave.

"You could have frozen to death out there," he said. "It's understandable that you could be confused."

Sunny wasn't confused. At least not about who and what she was. Although, if she was to be perfectly honest, there was something about Clint's closeness that stimulated strange, unfamiliar feelings. How was it, she wondered, that he could make her feel safe and unsettled all at the same time?

"I do feel a little strange," she admitted reluctantly. As his fairy godmother, she was supposed to be the one in charge here. Somehow, when she hadn't been paying close attention, things had definitely gotten out of hand.

Her soft voice wrapped around him like a velvet lariat. Gazing down into her eyes, which were twin pools of confusion, and something else he couldn't read, Clint felt that sensual hunger stir again.

Damn her! Didn't she realize that no woman in her right mind would look at a man that way, unless she wanted him to respond the way his mutinous body was responding?

Since she didn't seem in danger of dying from exposure, he wondered how the lady might respond if he suggested warming her up by taking her to bed where they could spend the rest of the snowy day driving each other crazy.

Crazy. That was, of course, the definitive word. Given the fact that she was claiming to be his fairy godmother was proof that she was one T-bone short of a steak fry. If that wasn't reason enough to keep his distance, the fact that he was even considering having sex with a total stranger who'd shown up at his front door proved that he was as nuts as she was.

"You'd better get out of those wet clothes," he muttered, backing away from her.

Although she was a great deal warmer than when he'd found her, Sunny still felt horribly disoriented. Of course, part of that could be because of how he was looking at her. His icy blue eyes, as they'd roamed over her face, had made her feel both hot and cold at the same time.

She'd reached the top of the stairs when she belatedly realized that she'd been responding to Clint like a mortal woman and suddenly remembered the impulsive wish she'd made right before rushing out into the storm.

She'd wished to be a real, mortal woman. Could it possibly be that somehow, that wish had been granted?

She went into the bedroom and looked at the suitcase she'd conjured up last night. It was about ten feet away, next to an overstuffed easy chair.

"Okay. Here goes." Concentrating as hard as she could, she blinked, intending to move the suitcase. When it remained steadfastly where it was, she tried again. Nothing.

"Oh, no."

Sunny sank down onto the bed as comprehension sank in. Now what? She cast a desperate gaze upward.

"Please," she whispered, "I didn't mean it. Not really."

She was not surprised when no answer was forthcoming.

Not having any idea what to do next, Sunny buried her face in her hands and began to weep.

Clint heard her sobs when he reached the top of the stairs. Terrific. That's all he needed. As if it wasn't bad enough, being stuck with a crazy woman who stirred up feelings he'd thought he'd buried with Laura, now he was confronted with a female in tears.

He stood in the open doorway; since her hands were covering her face, he was free to watch her undetected. She was sitting on the bed, her wet hair hanging over her shoulders, which were shaking with her wrenching sobs.

Pity stirred. Followed by desire, which reminded Clint exactly how long it had been since he'd touched a woman. Tasted a woman. Telling himself that the unruly feelings he'd been experiencing were nothing more than a basic case of horniness, he cleared his throat and entered the room.

"I brought you some tea."

Sunny's hands dropped to her lap. Her eyes flew open. "Tea?"

"Good thing you thought to pick some up at the store yesterday."

"Yes." He wasn't the only one who was surprised. Sunny couldn't remember blinking any tea into the pantry. Reminding herself that she wasn't exactly thinking clearly, she said, "That was lucky."

"I didn't know how you liked it. But I added some sugar."

"Thank you." She took the cup he practically shoved at her. "That's very considerate of you." Drawn by the aroma of the orange-spiced tea, she took a tentative sip and found it delicious. "This is wonderful."

"It's just a tea bag."

"I know." She smiled up at him. "But you've no idea how, given the right circumstances, even tea can taste like ambrosia."

"You must go nuts over champagne."

"I wouldn't know. Since I've never had any." She blew slightly, creating ripples in the dark amber drink, then took another longer sip.

Clint was about to suggest that they'd have to remedy that, when he managed to clamp his teeth together just in time.

"After you finish that tea, I'll go heat up last night's stew."

"Are you offering to fix me lunch?" That was such a turnaround from his previous behavior, Sunny couldn't believe she'd heard him correctly.

"I'd have the cook do it, but it's her day off. So I guess that leaves me."

"That's very nice of you." He wasn't really the unpleasant man he tried so hard to be, Sunny decided.

"Believe me, sweetheart, I'm never nice."

"That's right." Now that she was growing accustomed to it, Sunny found herself unfazed by his warning glare. "You're just trying to avoid having to explain to the sheriff how I starved to death in your house."

"Got it on the first try."

Clint felt the corner of his lips twitch. As he left the bedroom, he passed the mirror and was stunned to see he was smiling.

He wasn't the only one. Watching his reflection in the wall mirror, Sunny experienced a rush of pleasure so strong she almost laughed. She'd known he was a much kinder, gentler man than he appeared to be.

Unfortunately, although she suspected he'd argue the point, Laura had not been Clint's destiny. But the right woman was out there somewhere. All Sunny had to do was find her.

By the time she'd finished her tea, taken a hot shower and changed into some dry clothes, Sunny had regained her optimistic outlook on life. Refusing to believe that her superiors would have abandoned her here in this world without any magical powers, she'd come to the conclusion that somehow, her close brush with mortal death had affected her ability to tap into them.

"It's only a temporary glitch," she assured herself as she went downstairs to the kitchen. "It'll pass."

It had to. Because given Clint's less than cooperative attitude, she was going to need all the help she could get.

"YOU'RE NOT GOING to leave her alone down there?" Andromeda asked, stunned by Harmony's pronouncement that she'd done all she intended to do.

"Sunny will be fine." Harmony appeared unruffled.

"But you've taken away her magic."

"I've taken away her powers to change the physical world around her," the older woman agreed. "But, never fear, I've left her with all the magic she needs."

"What magic is that?"

"Her kind and generous spirit. Any man would be a fool not to fall in love with such a warmhearted woman."

"Clint Garvey isn't just any man."

"His own heart was once as open as Sunny's. It can be again. With her encouragement."

"I still don't understand. After all you did for Cinder-ella—"

"I do get so tired of hearing about her," Harmony snapped uncharacteristically. "Cindy was an unrelent-ingly sweet girl. But she wasn't exactly the most assertive young woman on the face of the planet. Or the most in-telligent."

"Yet she attracted the love of Prince Charming."

"As I said, she was sweet. And beautiful. But it took a great deal of work to get those two together. They were not," she confided, "a perfect match."

"Then why—"

"All right." Harmony sighed heavily. "I suppose it won't hurt for you to know the truth, after all these years. How-ever, you must promise to keep the story to yourself. I'd hate to encourage any of our new apprentices to behave so rashly."

"You could never be rash."

"That's what I thought. Until Sleeping Beauty's awakening."

"What?" Andromeda stared at her idol. "What does Sleeping Beauty have to do with Cinderella? Or, for that matter, Sunny?"

"This is going to be a long story," Harmony warned. "We may as well get comfortable."

With a single blink, she transported both women from the computer center to a lovely white wrought iron bench beneath a flowering apple tree in the contemplation garden. Nearby, a trio of fairies splashed gaily in the fountain, their gossamer wings glittering like gold dust in the morning sunshine.

She gathered her skirts around her. Her round face grew solemn. "Once upon a time," she began....

CLINT TILTED THE kitchen chair back, sipped his whiskey and glared out at the snow, which was continuing to fall outside the window. It was turning out to be one helluva storm, especially for one that hadn't even been predicted. At least none of the stock would freeze, thanks to Mariah.

He frowned as he thought of the woman who, in what seemed like another lifetime, had been his sister-in-law for less than a day. Lord knows, Mariah had had her own troubles. Troubles that had caused her to leave Whiskey River and become estranged from her sister for a decade. If it wasn't so tragic, he might have found it ironic that she'd returned home just hours too late to mend fences.

During the investigation, she'd been the only person who'd remained steadfastly in his corner; the only one who'd believed in his innocence, and who'd understood, at least somewhat, how he was suffering. She'd managed to put the murder behind her, had even married the sheriff whose job it had been to arrest him, and now Clint knew he was causing her additional pain.

Two weeks ago she'd dropped by to suggest that her crew round up his cattle along with her own stock, and take them down the mountain to more temperate winter pastures. That had been her excuse, and since he hadn't given any thought to the matter, Clint had accepted her offer and thanked her for thinking of it.

But now he realized that as real as her concern for his cattle had been, work had not been the only thing on her mind that day. Her real reason for visiting had been to try to shake him out of his depression. Unfortunately, all she'd done was make him feel more guilty. The memory of the concern on her lovely face was enough to make him want to refill his glass.

"It's lovely, isn't it?" a soft voice behind him offered.

His fingers tightened on the glass as he glanced back over his shoulder. "What?"

"The snow. It's like a fairyland."

Her smile lit up her eyes to a golden brown that reminded him of an aggie marble he'd had when he was a kid. It crossed his mind that most women might not consider that the most romantic analogy; of course, most women wouldn't understand how a twelve-year-old boy felt about his lucky shooter.

"You should know." He tossed back the whiskey, enjoying the way it burned as it went down. "Since you're a fairy godmother."

She sighed as she walked past him to stand by the window. "I made a mistake telling you that," she murmured,

Ambushed

seemingly as much to herself as to him. "I should have given you more time to get used to the idea."

He might not be at his best these days, but he sure as hell wasn't so far gone that he'd lost complete touch with reality. "Sweetheart, you could give me till the next millennium and I wouldn't believe that story."

She exhaled another soft, shimmering sigh. She'd changed into a petal pink sweater and matching leggings. Beneath the fluffy wool her shoulders were slumped, making her look almost as depressed as he felt. But, as he watched, she squared them decisively and turned around.

"Isn't it a little early in the day to begin drinking?"

"Isn't it a little early in the day to start nagging?" he countered. He was tempted to refill the glass again, just to show her he could. But sensing that this was a challenge of sorts, he resisted. "Shouldn't you be resting?"

"I'm fine. Really," she insisted when he appeared skeptical. "I'm much hardier than I look."

Which was a good thing, Clint decided. Since right now she looked a lot like the cotton candy he used to buy at the Mogollon County Fair when he was a kid. Soft, pink and deliciously sweet.

A silence settled over them as they stared across the room at each other. Sunny was the first to blink, and she lowered her eyes to the table. When she saw what was lying next to the now empty glass, her face went as white as the snow drifting down outside the window.

"You weren't thinking—"

"No." He picked up the revolver he'd brought in from the living room earlier, opened it and spun the cylinder. "It's unloaded."

Her relief was palpable. She made her way over to the table on legs that felt as if they'd turned to water, and sank down onto the chair across from him. "I'm sorry, I really don't mean to nag, but—"

"You don't want to be left with the job of scraping my brains off the wall behind the stove."

Color flooded into those too pale cheeks. "That's a horrible thing to think. And a cruel thing to say."

He felt a stab of guilt as he saw the hurt in her wide brown eyes. "Point taken. But then again, if you were to stay around here for any length of time, which you're not—" he warned when she looked inclined to interrupt "—you'd discover that I'm the kind of bastard given to cruel pronouncements."

"That's not true."

His brows dived down toward his nose. "Back in Whiskey River's early days, implying a man was a liar could get a person killed."

Ignoring the warning in his narrowed eyes, she reached out and placed her hand on his arm. "I was simply pointing out that you're a better man than you think you are, Clint Garvey."

He looked down at the hand on his sleeve. Her fingers were long and slender, the nails short and unpolished. The skin looked as soft as a baby's, suggesting that she'd never done manual labor. He remembered his mother's hands— roughened and red by years of hard work both indoor and out.

If Sunny was a housekeeper, he was the Prince of Wales.

"What's your last name?"

She blinked at the sudden change in subject. "Excuse me?"

"Your last name, sweetheart." He stroked a fingertip up the back of her hand and discovered that the ivory skin was, indeed, every bit as soft as it looked. "If we're going to be stuck here together, I'd like to know exactly who I'm snowbound with."

Although his touch wasn't overtly threatening, Sunny felt strangely frightened. "Didn't I tell you?"

"No." His fingers slipped beneath the sleeve of her sweater. "Not that I recall. But just in case I've forgotten, why don't you refresh my memory?"

She bit her lip and weighed her options. One of the reasons Sunny hated lying was that such behavior was so foreign to her nature, she always found it impossible to keep her stories straight. Which is why, more often than not, she'd find herself caught up in a hopelessly tangled web of her own making.

Sensing that Clint was not going to be easy to deceive, she decided that the safest tactic would be to continue to hedge as long as possible. At least until they could get out of here and she could find him a suitable wife.

"I don't remember."

His answering stare was razor sharp.

"Really," she insisted, afraid he could hear the falsehood in her desperate tone. "The shock of my recent ordeal must have affected my memory."

He surprised her by laughing. A rough, harsh, rusty bark that sounded as if it had been a very long time since anything—or anyone—had made him laugh.

Turning his attention to the Colt again, he traced the engraving on the butt with his finger. "This was my great-great-grandfather's cavalry revolver."

"Family heirlooms are nice." Although she was grateful for the change in subject, unloaded or not, she wished he'd put the gun down.

"He came home from fighting in the Civil War and found his wife dead of a fever," he said as if he hadn't heard her soft comment. "I always thought it was damn ironic that he made it through that brutal war without a scratch only to have her die while he was riding back home."

"That was a tragic coincidence."

"The timing sure as hell sucked. He made her casket himself, with the pine he'd been saving to use for a cradle. Then he went out to the back meadow, and dug a hole beneath the tree where she'd liked to picnic in the summer."

As he stared out the window, Sunny suspected he was not looking at the driving snow, but imagining the long-ago scene. When the microwave dinged, he shook his head, as if to rid his mind of depressing visions. He spooned the reheated stew into two bowls and put them on the table along with a plate stacked with thick slices of last night's bread.

Clint continued his story as they ate.

"According to William's journal, after he dug the hole, he returned to the house and bathed her with warm water scented with lilacs. Remembering that scent had helped him overcome the battleground stench of rotting flesh and blood during those war years."

His voice had taken on a distant, faraway tone, making Sunny wonder if he even remembered she was in the room. "He brushed her hair with the ivory-handled brush he'd given her before they were married. She'd brushed her long black hair with that brush and he'd watched her as he lay on the bed in her room on the second floor of the Golden Belle Dance Hall and Saloon. When she smiled at him in the mirror, William knew he was in love."

"She worked there?" Sunny asked. Although the documents in the file she'd been given had referred to William's wife's tragic death, it hadn't mentioned her being a prostitute.

"That's right. William's wife was a whore." His challenging gaze dared her to criticize his ancestor.

"If you're trying to shock me, it's going to take more than that," she told him mildly. "Tell me the rest of the story."

He gave her another long look. Then, since she seemed genuinely interested, he shrugged and continued. "It took some convincing, but Annie finally agreed to marry him. And although life in Arizona Territory proved a lot harder than her pampered existence as the most sought after working girl in San Francisco, if William's journal can be believed, she never complained. In fact, he wrote that not a day went by that she didn't assure him in words and in bed, how much she loved him."

"That's a lovely story," Sunny said. "And you're so fortunate that your great-great-grandfather left behind the journal for you." It was, she considered, a much nicer legacy than that deadly gun lying beside his plate.

"William was reputed to be an outspoken man who didn't bother censoring his words. He was every bit as frank in his journal," Clint stated.

"He even wrote about how he'd wept like a baby while he dressed her in the lace-trimmed nightgown he'd so enjoyed taking off her. Wept as he'd held her in his arms one last time. Wept as he'd put her in the casket that was to be her final resting place, then lowered the pine box into the ground and covered it with earth."

When he fell silent, his face set in a granite mask so full of pain that it was all Sunny could do to keep from weeping herself, she knew he was thinking about another woman's death. A woman he'd never been allowed to love openly. A woman he'd been deprived of holding one final time in his arms, of kissing goodbye before she was buried on the neighboring land.

Clint dragged his hand down his face and let out a long, pained breath. "He said the only prayer he knew," he continued in a low gruff monotone, as if determined to get through the story. "It was one he'd heard the chaplain use over too many men on too many battlefields—The Lord's Prayer. Then he went back into the house where he proceeded to get very, very drunk."

"A not uncommon reaction," she said.

He gave her a sharp look, but her tone and her expression held not an iota of censure. "I suppose not."

"What happened next?" Sunny prompted.

"The next morning, he saddled up and rode off to join the cavalry. No longer having anything to live for, he figured that at least if he died in the Indian wars, he'd be reunited with his Annie."

"But he didn't die."

"Nope." He shook his head. "Fate proved a damn fickle mistress yet again when he was mustered out of the 7th Cavalry three days before General Custer led his troops into the Little Bighorn."

"He was lucky."

"Perhaps. Or, maybe he had a fairy godmother looking after him."

"That always helps," she agreed, once again ignoring his obvious sarcasm.

Clint gave her another long steady look. "Hell, it was probably your great-great grandmother."

"You never know," she said mildly.

She was either nuts, or the smoothest scam artist he'd ever met. Clint, who'd always considered himself a pretty good judge of both horseflesh and people, couldn't decide which.

"So, what happened after he left the army?" Sunny asked.

"Since he didn't have anywhere else to go, he returned here to Arizona Territory and married a young widow who bore him three children, one of whom—the son—reached adulthood."

"Your great-grandfather."

"Yeah."

"How wonderful that he was able to fall in love again," Sunny said encouragingly, hoping he'd see this parallel between his great-great-grandfather and himself.

"Spoken like a true romantic," Clint replied in a remote voice. He pushed away from the table, stood up and without another word, walked out of the room. Taking the gun with him.

Unwilling to leave him alone to try to commit suicide again, Sunny was right on his heels.

He stopped in front of the open bathroom door. "I'm going to take a shower. If you insist on following me, I suppose I could always use a little help with that spot in the middle of my back that's so hard to reach."

He was so tall. So strong. So threatening. So compelling. Sunny swallowed. "If that's supposed to frighten me away, it's not working."

"What if I'm not trying to scare you away?" His eyes on hers, he trailed a fingertip down her cheek. "What if I was inviting you to share my shower with me?"

"Thanks, but I've already showered." The smile she flashed him was bright and as false as fool's gold.

He looked down at her for a long silent time. Sunny stood her ground, refusing to flinch. Finally she was rewarded when she caught sight of the twitch at the corners of his lips.

He might refuse to admit it, but he was softening. She could sense it. Emboldened by the knowledge, she reached up and patted his stubbly cheek.

"You might think about shaving while you're at it," she suggested sweetly.

That said, it was her turn to walk away.

5

"I CAN'T BELIEVE you did such a thing!" Andromeda stared in amazement at the most famous fairy godmother of all. To think that the normally unflappable Harmony would lose her temper and make a bet that she could successfully match two woefully incompatible individuals was astonishing.

"Sometimes, I can't either," Harmony admitted as she finished up her story. "But I was younger then, and unfortunately possessed of a flash-fire temper.

"And Merryweather was so irritating, always going on so about how she'd managed to rescue Sleeping Beauty by changing Maleficent's death sentence to merely sleeping until she was awakened by a prince's kiss, that I wanted—no, I needed—to show her up."

"By pulling off the mismatch of the century."

"Well, you have to admit, I succeeded."

"No one has ever topped you," Andromeda agreed.

"Believe me, I'm all too aware of that. And, although I rather enjoy the adulation of our young romance godmothers, and the statue in the contemplation garden is quite attractive, I do regret not being able to keep my hand in, so to speak."

Harmony's merry eyes turned wistful. "Unfortunately, there weren't any matches I could have made that would have lived up to the impossible standard I inadvertently set for myself."

"Matching Sunny with Clint Garvey could do that," Andromeda said. "If it works."

"It is a risk," Harmony reluctantly agreed. "Which is why you're the only one who knows I'm attempting it. If Sunny and her cowboy live happily ever after, then you can announce it at our monthly awards dinner. If the match doesn't work out, no one will be the wiser."

"You know," Andromeda suggested, "it might have a better chance if I could talk to Sunny face-to-face. Explain what was happening."

Good manners and tradition, going back to the beginning of time, decreed that one fairy godmother never interfere with another's chosen assignment. Yet, knowing Sunny as she did, Andromeda couldn't share Harmony's confidence about the plan.

"Surely you don't want to reveal that she's her assignment's chosen mate?"

"Of course not. But she's bound to be feeling a little unsettled right now. Perhaps if I could just reassure her—"

Harmony laughed. "If there's one thing Sunny has an abundance of, it's self-assurance. Even when it's misplaced.

"However," Harmony added, "given Sunny's past history, I can certainly understand your concern. Perhaps it might be a good idea to calm any fears she might have. Goodness knows she's unpredictable enough even without this extra burden."

More than a little relieved, Andromeda folded her hands together in front of her and imagined herself in Clint Garvey's kitchen.

Sunny was whistling an off-tune rendition of "Jingle Bells" as she managed to tidy up the kitchen. Outside the window the snow had finally stopped and the afternoon sun slanting through the white-flocked pine trees made the landscape sparkle like diamonds. The scene, which could have come straight from the front of a Christmas card, glittered as brightly as the hope in her heart.

A faint sound, like the silver bells in the Christmas song, captured her attention and she spun around. "Oh, I'm so glad to see you!" she exclaimed.

As serious as things were, Andromeda couldn't help smiling. So many of the community complained about Sunny's mismatches. Unfortunately, none of those naysayers seemed to realize that her boundless enthusiasm was contagious. Their world was going to be a slightly darker—not to mention duller—place without Sunny in it.

"I'm always with you," she remarked calmly. "You should know that."

"I'd hoped you were," Sunny admitted. "But then, after I foolishly made that wish to be mortal . . ."

"That was careless of you," the older woman agreed in that faintly chiding tone Sunny had become accustomed to hearing.

"I know." Sunny's soft sigh ruffled her curly bangs. "But I was so worried about Clint that I just didn't think."

"You were leading with your heart again. And not your head."

"True." Sunny's smile faded slightly. "But it's so difficult not to open my heart to Clint. He's such a special man. And he's suffered so horribly."

"You knew that when you accepted the assignment," Andromeda reminded her.

"I know." The light momentarily left Sunny's bright eyes, like a candle being snuffed out by an icy wind. "But I believe I've found the answer to my dilemma."

Andromeda arched a brow. "What's that?"

"This." Sunny held out the letter she'd found lying beside the kitchen wastebasket. It looked as if Clint had wadded it up into a ball and tossed it in the general direction of the wicker basket, but missed. Undoubtedly, because of all the alcohol he'd been drinking.

Andromeda gingerly plucked the letter from Sunny's outstretched hand, and frowned at the coffee ring in the center of the paper. "This is a notice about a rodeo."

"In Tombstone! Clint is being invited to defend his bull-riding championship."

"So it says." Andromeda's frown deepened. "I don't understand what this has to do with you—"

"Don't you see, women love cowboys! All I have to do is get Clint to agree to take part in the contest, then find a suitable mate—a woman with interests similar to his—and get them together."

Sunny's smile was back to full wattage and warm enough, were she so inclined, to melt all the snow that had fallen.

"I suppose that's one way to handle things." Poor dear. She was as clueless as ever. Didn't she realize that she didn't have to convince the man to go anywhere? That destiny—and, more importantly, Harmony—had decreed that she was the perfect match for Clint Garvey?

"It's the best way," Sunny assured her. "There is just one little problem."

"Oh?" Andromeda tilted her head and tried to appear curious as she wondered how much of all this she should explain.

"I seem to have lost my powers."

There was a long, drawn out pause. Despite her regrettable romance record, Sunny was an intelligent young woman. She'd eventually figure things out.

"I know, dear," the older woman finally said. "And believe me, it wasn't my idea, but . . ."

Sunny felt her heart plummet to her stomach. "The committee has taken away my powers?"

"I'm afraid so." All right, so it wasn't exactly the committee, but there was no point in making the poor girl feel worse by telling her the truth.

Sunny wrung her hands as she began to pace the shiny kitchen floor. "But how am I supposed to save Clint if I don't have any powers?"

"You're a clever girl. You'll think of something."

"I don't believe this." Sunny sank defeatedly down onto a chair by the kitchen table and dropped her head into her hands. A long silence settled over the room. When she finally lifted her gaze, her eyes were bleaker than her superior had ever seen them. "They want to ensure that I don't succeed."

"Oh no, dear, that's not it at all."

"Of course it is." Sunny sighed, then began thoughtfully tapping a fingernail on the tabletop. It would take a miracle to pull this off without her powers. "Someone is bound and determined to drum me out of romance," she concluded. Which wasn't surprising, considering all the failure slips in her permanent record. "But you know what?"

"What?" Andromeda asked cautiously, fearing the answer.

"It isn't going to work." Sunny stood up and resumed her pacing. "I'm not going to leave that poor man without someone to love! It's not fair. Oh, he's a little gruff, but he's a good man, deep down inside. He deserves to be happy." She spun back toward her superior, her hands splayed on her hips, bright pink flags of determination flying in her cheeks. "And I refuse to allow any bureaucrats in Fairy

Godmother Central to keep me from finding him the perfect mate."

"Brava, dear." Andromeda clapped her approval.

It did not escape Andromeda's notice that during her impassioned monologue, Sunny had not once mentioned her own motive for succeeding with this assignment. Somehow, when she hadn't been looking, her focus had shifted from her own agenda to Clint's needs.

Perhaps Harmony had been right, after all. Perhaps Sunny's destiny was here, with this man.

"I have faith in you, Sunny." Although physical touch was not a part of their world, some instinct made the older woman run her hand down Sunny's bright hair. "And now, before I go, I'm going to leave you with a little gift."

"A gift?" Hope flooded into Sunny's eyes. "You're going to restore my powers?"

"I'm afraid I can't do that. But I can give you three wishes."

"Three wishes?" Sunny immediately thought of Clint's earlier sarcastic crack about genies.

"Yes. That's truly all I can do. So, you must be very careful to use them wisely."

"Three wishes," Sunny repeated.

It wasn't much. Certainly not as helpful as having her powers restored. Then again, she reminded herself, three wishes were definitely better than nothing at all.

"Thank you." In a burst of gratitude, she flung her arms around this woman who'd been in her corner for so long, supporting her when others would have given up trying.

Sunny felt a fleeting sense of loss when Andromeda slipped out of the enthusiastic embrace and began to fade away.

"I promise," Sunny called out, "I won't disappoint you this time."

There was no answer. But Sunny didn't mind. Because now that she had three wishes as backup to her clever rodeo plan, everything should work out wonderfully!

Her heart light, her spirits renewed, she went into the pantry. When she viewed the shelves filled with far more food than she'd stocked them with yesterday, she looked upward, her face wreathed in a smile. "Thank you!"

Her confidence high, Sunny began to plan dinner. Just like a mortal woman might for the man in her life.

Clint heard her singing as he came down the stairs. Her voice was a pure clear contralto that was horrendously off-key. He felt the unfamiliar tug of his lips trying to smile again.

She'd put a white chef's apron over her soft sweater and had pulled her hair back into a haphazard knot to keep it out of the mixture she was stirring. He stood in the doorway and watched her for a time, trying not to think about how often he'd pictured Laura in just this way. As always, the mental image caused a deep low ache in his gut.

A low sound, like the moan of a wounded wolf, drew Sunny's instant attention. "Oh, don't you look nice," she said encouragingly, ignoring the nicks on his chin. "I like that sweater."

He glanced down to see what, exactly, he was wearing; it was the first thing he'd pulled from the drawer and he hadn't paid any attention. "Laura gave it to me. For my birthday."

"The blue matches your eyes exactly. Obviously, she had very good taste."

"Of course she did. She picked me, didn't she?" He crossed the room, took a glass from the shelf and was about to pour a glass of whiskey, but stopped suddenly and exchanged the glass for a coffee cup.

Sunny noted the change of mind, was pleased, and clever enough not to comment on it. "Don't look now, Clint," she said instead, "but I believe you just made a joke."

"Damn." He pulled the pack of cigarettes out of his pocket, shook one loose and lit it with a kitchen match from the box on the counter. "I'll have to be more careful in the future."

And that statement was, Sunny decided, another one. Things were definitely looking up! "I thought I'd bake a cake," she said as she resumed stirring the dark brown batter. "I hope you like chocolate."

"Who doesn't?"

She took some pans from a bottom cupboard and greased them with butter. "Would you like to lick the bowl when I'm done?"

He smoked and watched as she dusted the pans with too much flour, creating a white cloud. "I'll just wait for the final product."

"Whatever you want." She poured the batter into the pans, then carried them carefully to the oven. She was so intent on getting them on the rack without spilling the batter, she didn't notice Clint coming up behind her.

"Whatever I want?" the deep voice rumbled in her ear. "What if I want you?"

She managed to shut the door, then turned around. "I was talking about the cake—"

"You've got flour on your face."

"I said I was a good cook," she said, feeling strangely entranced by the lambent flame in his eyes. "I don't recall saying I was neat."

"Actually, it's kinda cute . . . there's a little bit here." He ran the back of his fingers along the line of her jaw, then touched her cheek. "And here."

"Clint—" His touch created sparks on skin that already felt uncomfortably warm. It had to be the heat of the oven, Sunny assured herself. It couldn't be anything else.

"I like the way you say my name." He ground the now unwanted cigarette out in a nearby ashtray, then lowered his head. His lips brushed the sensitive hollow behind her earlobe. "In that throaty little voice, tinged with desire. And just a touch of fear." He nipped at her earlobe, his teeth tugging gently. "Are you afraid of me, Sunny?"

"Of course not," she stammered weakly, as she tried to back away. But he kept moving toward her, effectively fencing her in between the countertop and his body.

"Liar." His mouth moved to her temple, beneath the froth of gilt curls.

Clint Garvey was like no other man she'd ever been assigned. He burned with a ferocious intensity that, in all honesty, did frighten her. Just a little.

"This isn't going to work," she warned as he threaded his hands through her unruly waves.

She had the most amazing hair. It felt like silk, smelled like a mountain meadow in wildflower season and gleamed like a blazing noontime sun on the Fourth of July. It was the kind of hair a man could wallow in.

"What isn't going to work?" He skimmed his fingers down her neck.

"Trying to frighten me away." Her heart picked up its beat as his palms smoothed over her shoulders, turning her muscles to mush. "Because I'm not going."

"You sound pretty sure of yourself." His hands slid down her arms, his long fingers encircled her wrists, holding her hostage. "When is it going to sink through that bright blond head of yours that I'm the one calling the shots around here?"

Sunny's mouth had gone so dry she had to swallow before she could speak. "You need me." Her voice, usually so steady, was soft and raspy and thick with the turbulent emotions she couldn't comprehend.

His grin was quick and decidedly lascivious. "You called that one right, sweetheart." He moved even closer, until the tile counter was digging into her back and he was pressed against her, so closely that she could feel his heart thudding within the strong wall of his chest.

Her mind clouded, her blood swam as the friction between his aroused male body and her own strangely restless one threatened to set them both on fire.

"You need me," she agreed, trying to tug her hand loose from his restraint. "But not this way. I told you, I came here to be your housekeeper."

"That was yesterday. Today you're my fairy godmother, remember?"

"I need to explain about that—"

"It doesn't matter." His voice was rough and raw. Anger flared as he viewed the edgy, yet strangely innocent desire in her dazed eyes.

The lady was emotional quicksand. Clint figured it was his recent penchant for self-destruction that had drawn him to her. That and the inescapable fact that his throbbing body had completely disconnected itself from his mind.

He shook his head to clear it of the hot, unruly thoughts he had no business thinking, let go of her wrists and moved back a step. "As soon as the road clears, I'm taking you back to town."

"And if I refuse to leave?"

Good question. Short of physically dragging her out of his house, he wasn't sure what he could do. "I suppose I

could call the sheriff and have him arrest you for tres-
passing," he mused out loud.

"You wouldn't do it."

"You sound awfully sure about that."

"I am."

There was a long silence as Clint stared down at her.
"Hell," he said finally.

"Does that mean I get the job?"

Even as he told himself he'd be crazy to let this woman
sleep under the same roof as him, the aroma of baking cake
teased at his senses, weakening his resolve. "It means I
suppose it wouldn't hurt to give it a try. For a few days."

Now that she'd won the little battle of wills, Sunny
could afford to be gracious. She also decided this was not
the time to bring up the rodeo in Tombstone. Clint was a
man accustomed to making his own decisions, and she'd
just have to make him believe that defending his championship was his own idea.

"Thank you," she said solemnly, managing, with effort, to restrain the triumphant smile that was trying to
break free. "You won't be sorry."

"That's probably what the captain of the *Titanic* said
when he was greeting the boarding passengers," Clint
muttered. "You should know, right off the bat, that I can't
afford to pay much. I know people think ranchers are rich,
but—"

"I don't need any money."

"Oh, excuse me. I forgot. As a fairy godmother, you can
just wiggle that cute little nose and conjure up piles of
dough."

"Normally, that would be the case," Sunny agreed, deciding that to point out that fairy godmothers didn't twitch
would only get them off track. "However, there was this
little glitch and I'm afraid I've lost my powers."

"Oh really?" He folded his arms. "Talk about rotten timing. So, I guess this means you're not going to be able to give me a demonstration?"

Sunny thought about her three wishes and decided that wasting one just to uphold her pride and prove she was what she said she was would be terribly foolhardy, even for her.

"I'm afraid not."

"Too bad." Surprising her yet again, he ducked his head and brushed a quick kiss against her pouting lips. "Don't worry, sweetheart," he said. "I always thought that bibbi-ty-bobbity-boo stuff was overrated, anyway."

The brief flare of heat from his kiss sent shock waves all the way down to Sunny's toes. She pressed her fingertips against her tingling lips, watching as he pulled the jacket from the hook by the door.

"Where are you going?"

"Now that it's stopped snowing, I'm going to get a shovel from the barn, dig the truck out and finish fixing the tire. Then I've got some errands to run in town. Do you want me to pick anything up?"

"Pick anything up?"

"Groceries, cleaning supplies, anything like that?"

"Oh." Sunny was, quite literally, stumped. She had no idea what a mortal housekeeper might need. "Why don't you just get some basics?" she suggested, hoping he wouldn't ask her to be more specific.

She was more than a little relieved when he merely shrugged and agreed. Sunny watched as he waded through the drifts of snow toward the barn.

Then she set to work, cleaning up the bowls and beaters, finding the task much more difficult when forced to do it the mortal way.

6

THIRTY MINUTES AFTER Clint had driven off to town, a fire-engine red Jeep Cherokee pulled into the driveway, a thick evergreen tied to the roof. Sunny, up to her elbows in soapsuds, watched out the kitchen window as three women got out of the Jeep. A moment later, the doorbell rang.

Catching a glimpse of her reflection in the toaster, Sunny sighed. She was, to put it charitably, a mess. Her hair had sprung loose of its clip and the front of her apron was spattered with chocolate from the fudge frosting she'd made. Drying her hands on the apron which was already wet from washing dishes, she went to answer the door.

"Hello," a visibly pregnant woman said with a polite smile. "I'm Noel Giraudeau—"

"Princess of Montacroix," Sunny acknowledged, recognizing her immediately.

"Formerly of Montacroix," Noel corrected easily. "I've been living in Whiskey River for several months." She nodded toward the auburn-haired woman on her left. "This is Tara Delaney. And this," she said, turning to the woman on her right, "is Mariah Callahan."

"Hi," Tara Delaney greeted her with a friendly smile. But Sunny, who was getting intensely strong vibes from the trio, feared she viewed a flash of recognition in the woman's green eyes. Which was impossible, she assured herself. On all the other occasions she'd come to earth, mortals had never realized she wasn't really one of them.

"Hello." Although Mariah Callahan's expression was polite, her tone was as chilly as the weather.

"Please, come in," Sunny invited.

"Is Clint home?" Noel asked as the trio entered the house.

"I'm afraid not, he's driven into town for supplies, but—"

"I don't mean to be rude," Mariah broke into Sunny's explanation, "but may I ask who, exactly, you are? And what you're doing in Clint's house?"

"Oh. I'm sorry." Sunny held out her hand. "I'm Sunny, uh—" her mind whirled, seeking a last name "—Snow," she said as she glanced past the women before shutting the door. "And I'm Clint's new housekeeper."

Mariah ignored the outstretched hand, her lapse in manners drawing a puzzled glance from Noel. "I didn't know Clint was looking for a housekeeper."

Mariah Callahan's hostility was more than obvious. Realizing that this was the sainted Laura's sister, Sunny decided that it was only natural for her to be resentful of anyone who appeared to be taking Laura's place. Although all three women were beautiful, Mariah was the most stunningly desirable woman Sunny had ever seen. If her older sister had possessed even a hint of Mariah Callahan's feminine appeal, the task of finding Clint a new woman to love had just gotten a whole lot tougher.

"I answered his ad in the *Rim Rock Record*," Sunny said.

"Really?" It was Noel's turn to look surprised. "I hadn't realized Clint had placed an ad. My fiancé—" she informed Sunny "—is publisher of the *Record*."

"Which doesn't mean he proofreads every classified ad," Tara countered.

"True," Noel agreed absently, looking at Sunny with renewed interest. Sunny watched as something flickered in the princess's blue eyes. She also noticed Noel's quick questioning glance toward Tara, who seemed to answer with a faint, almost imperceptible nod of her head.

"Would you like some coffee?" Sunny asked.

"We wouldn't want to interrupt your cleaning," Noel said.

"How did you know—"

"Your apron gave you away." Tara smiled. "And we'd love some tea. Mariah's stomach was a bit queasy on the ride over here and— "

"And I'm fine now," Mariah broke in sharply. There was no mistaking her tone or her attitude. Sunny could serve her Earl Grey on a silver platter with freshly baked pastries, and she still wouldn't be able to win Mariah Swann Callahan's approval.

"It's no trouble," Sunny insisted. "If you'd just like to go into the living room—"

"The kitchen will be fine," Noel said. "It's so much cozier, don't you think?"

"We should be going," Mariah argued stubbornly. "You have a doctor's appointment soon."

"Not for another hour and a half." The warm smile Noel gave Sunny was a decided contrast to her cool, pale blond appearance. "Everyone has been hovering over me for months."

"It's not hovering to make certain the doctor examines you," Mariah snapped. "After all, Noel, you're due today."

"Today?" Sunny's startled gaze dropped to Noel's abdomen.

"First babies are always late. I'll be fine." That seemed to settle the matter, and although Mariah looked less than pleased, the women followed Sunny into the kitchen.

Sunny filled the kettle with water, placed it on the stove, and silently thanked Andromeda for the tea bags in the pantry cupboard. "I think I have some cookies around here somewhere." She began rummaging around on a shelf for the box she was sure she'd seen earlier.

"How long have you been a housekeeper?" Mariah asked suddenly.

"I arrived here yesterday."

"I was referring to your previous work. I assume you have references?"

"Of course," Sunny lied blithely, relieved when the phone on the wall suddenly rang. She picked it up. "Hello? Oh, yes, she's here."

She held out the phone toward Noel. "It's Mac."

Noel sighed. "What a surprise. It's been at least five minutes since he last checked in." She took the receiver Sunny was holding out to her. "No, darling," she said, "no pains yet."

She rolled her eyes as she listened to what were obviously words of husbandly concern. "I promise, the moment I feel so much as a twinge, I'll call you...."

"Of course I'm not alone. Tara and Mariah are keeping a close eye on me. Yes, they have the numbers for the hospital and the doctor, but I'm sure I'll be able to make the calls myself." Another pause. "Yes, dear. I know, just in case."

She put her hand over the mouthpiece and grinned at her friends. "I'm to give you the number of Mac's pager. In case he has to leave the office."

Tara laughed. And even Mariah smiled.

"Goodbye, darling," Noel said. "Yes, I promise. Yes. First thing. Now, if you don't let me go, I'm going to embarrass myself. Yes, I love you, too." She hung up and turned to Sunny. "I hate to ask, but if I could use your bathroom—"

"Of course. I'll show you—"

"Oh, don't bother, I know where it is. And your tea water's ready." She'd no sooner spoken than the kettle began its strident whistle.

Sunny poured the four cups of tea and served them with the chocolate mint Girl Scout cookies she'd located. She'd just put the plate on the table when the princess returned.

"Is everything all right?" Tara asked.

"I keep telling everyone I'm fine. Gracious, you'd think I was the first woman in the world to have a baby."

"You may not be the first," Sunny said, "but it's a miracle every time a child comes into the world."

"That's so true," Noel replied softly. She seemed lost in a pleasant memory for a moment, then returned to her brisk self. "The reason we came here today," she said, "was to bring Clint a tree."

"A tree?"

"A Christmas tree," Mariah said. "We didn't think he'd get one on his own."

"I don't believe he's in a very festive mood," Sunny allowed.

"That's not surprising," Mariah returned sharply. "After all, the poor guy lost the only woman he'd ever loved. The only woman he will ever love."

Sunny got Mariah's message loud and clear. Clint had always loved Laura, always would, and only a fool would think he'd ever be able to care for another woman. Understanding that Mariah had obviously loved her sister very much, Sunny was not offended. Neither was she going to allow Mariah Callahan to deter her from her assignment.

"It was a tragic loss," she agreed. "But it was Laura who was killed. Not Clint."

The challenge had been met and countered. An expectant silence settled over the kitchen as everyone waited to see how Mariah would respond.

"You don't know Clint like I do."

"That's true." Sunny's nerves were tense, nevertheless she forced her most sincere smile. "But I do know that it's not good for him to be dwelling on the past so much."

Mariah arched a gilt brow and looked about to argue when Sunny added, "And I'm sure, as his friend, you want him to be happy again."

"Of course I do," Mariah answered.

"We all do," Noel agreed.

"Which is why we brought the tree," Tara said, returning the conversation to the reason for the women's visit in the first place. "We were hoping to get him to at least acknowledge the holiday."

"Especially after he stood us up for Thanksgiving dinner."

"I think the tree is a lovely idea," Sunny told them. "And I'm sure he'll appreciate the gesture."

That little matter taken care of, Noel, who seemed to be the spokesperson for the group, deftly steered the conversation into safer waters, informing Sunny of the upcoming Whiskey River Christmas tree-lighting ceremony and Santa Claus parade. From there they went on to a brief discussion of the weather and the sudden early blizzard that seemed to have caught all the area weather forecasters by surprise.

As she sipped her tea, Sunny began to relax and enjoy the feminine companionship. "Do any of you know a woman named Charmayne Hunter?" she asked suddenly.

Noel and Tara shook their heads. Mariah's gaze sharpened. "I know Charmayne." Her tone did not suggest she liked her. "Why?"

"I heard the name mentioned in town," Sunny lied. The truth was she'd read it in Clint's file. "I went to school with a Charmayne Hunter and thought perhaps it might be the same person."

"Well, it isn't. Charmayne grew up in Whiskey River. I think I heard she's living in Las Vegas now, teaching barrel racing. She also had a thing going with Clint for a while. That is what you're asking about, isn't it?"

The challenge hung between them. Sunny decided to meet it head-on. "You don't like me very much, do you?"

"I don't know you."

"True." Sunny fiddled with her spoon for a moment, framing her response. "Would it make any difference," she murmured, "if I told you that my only interest in Clint is that he's happy?"

"That's all any of us want," Noel said smoothly, placing her hand on Mariah's arm, as if silently counseling restraint. She glanced up at the kitchen wall clock, then turned to the others. "Since the road's undoubtedly still going to be a bit icy, I suppose we'd better take the tree off the car roof and get going."

Sunny followed them outside, and helped Tara and Mariah unload the heavy tree and lean it up against the side of the house. "It's lovely," she said, envisioning it covered with bright white lights, glass balls and tinsel. She turned toward Mariah. "Is it from your land?"

"Actually, it is. Trace and I found it in a spot where Laura and Clint used to meet when they were younger. Before our father caught them and made them break it off."

Once again, the message was all too clear. Clint belonged to Laura. It didn't matter that the woman was dead; her sister was going to ensure that he remained steadfastly loyal.

"I'll tell him you brought it by," Sunny said.

The two women exchanged a brief, challenging look. Then, without a word, Mariah turned and walked back around the Jeep and climbed into the driver's seat.

"She's still a little sensitive when it comes to Laura," Tara explained. "I don't know how much you know—"

"I know everything."

"Oh." Tara and Noel exchanged another brief glance. "Well, then, you can understand this is difficult for her. Finding another woman living with Clint."

"I'm living in Clint's house," Sunny said. "Which is not really the same as living with him."

"That's true." Noel agreed. "And I'm certain Mariah will get used to the idea. Personally, I'm relieved that Clint has someone to watch out for him. We've all been terribly worried."

"He's going to be all right," Sunny promised.

"Yes." Once again Noel's smile suggested that she was finding something faintly humorous about all this. "I believe he's in very good hands."

"It was nice meeting you, Sunny," Tara said. "Oh, and I'm having a little get-together next Thursday evening. Nothing fancy, just friendly conversation. Can we count on you and Clint?"

There was no way Sunny was going to spend an evening with Laura's sister. "I can't answer for Clint, but—"

"Oh, of course you can," Tara insisted. "For heaven's sake, Sunny, just say you'll come. And Noel and I promise that Mariah will be on her best behavior."

From what she had seen, Sunny decided, controlling Mariah Callahan would take a whip and a chair.

"Why don't you give it some thought," Noel suggested when she didn't immediately answer.

"All right." Sunny doubted many people could say no to the lovely pregnant princess. "I'll think about it."

"Good." Noel nodded, seemingly satisfied for now. Tara climbed into the back seat. Just as Noel was about to get into the front passenger seat, she turned toward Sunny. "Oh, and I believe you'll find it much easier to use the dishwasher, rather than do all those dishes by hand."

"Dishwasher?"

"It's next to the sink. I'm sure you'll be able to find an instruction book somewhere in the kitchen. If not, just give me a call. I'm in the book."

She shut the door. As if more than a little eager to leave, Mariah gunned the motor.

As she stood on the porch, watching the Jeep drive away from the house, Sunny asked herself, what, if anything, Noel knew about her situation.

She also wondered what her odds were of getting away with not telling Clint about the invitation.

"She seemed nice," Tara commented as they drove down the curving road toward Whiskey River.

"If she's a housekeeper, I'm Princess Di," Mariah muttered.

Noel glanced over at the woman who'd been so quick to befriend her when she'd first arrived in Whiskey River. "If I didn't know you better, I'd think you were jealous."

"Why don't you just read my mind?" Mariah suggested grimly.

Mariah was one of the few people in Whiskey River, along with Tara and Jessica Ingersoll, the county attorney, who knew of Noel's psychic abilities.

"You know I have better manners than that," Noel answered mildly.

"Surely you don't want Clint to spend the rest of his life alone," Tara said.

"What I want is for you to cast a spell over that blond interloper and send her back to wherever it is she came from."

"I don't do spells," Tara reminded her.

"But you could, if you wanted to."

"I suppose I could. But when I decided to claim my grandmother's house and take over her herbal mail-order business, I also made the decision not to follow in her Druidic footsteps."

"That's a damn waste, if you ask me," Mariah muttered. "If I could do magic—"

"Sunny can," Noel said suddenly.

"What?" Mariah shot her a startled look. "Are you saying she's a witch? Like Tara?"

"She's not a witch." Noel's eyes became thoughtful. "But there's something there." She glanced back at Tara. "You sensed it too, didn't you?"

Tara nodded. "I sensed something. But it was very vague and she was doing a good job of blocking the vibrations. But if she was really capable of casting spells, surely she'd use one to wash those dishes."

"You don't," Noel said.

"Only because I've always wanted to live like an ordinary woman."

"Maybe Sunny has made the same decision."

"Perhaps."

A silence settled over the inside of the Jeep. Mariah was the first to break it. "This is just terrific." Her tone said otherwise. "So, if you two are right, Clint's living with a woman capable of casting a spell over him."

"Oh, I don't think she's going to need magic to do that," Noel murmured.

Mariah's answer to that was a ripe, pungent curse.

CLINT FELT AS if he were on display as he pushed the cart around the market. It seemed everyone in town wanted to talk to him, and those who didn't were gathered in close little clutches, obviously talking *about* him. He'd gotten used to the stares during those bleak days when he'd been the chief suspect in Laura's murder. At the time he'd been too shell-shocked to give a damn what anyone thought about him.

Later, after the shock of her death had worn off, leaving him with only that mind-drugging depression, he'd come to hate the looks of sympathy—and even worse, pity—he was forced to put up with whenever he came into town. It crossed his mind that even three days ago, garnering so much attention would have made him abandon his groceries and walk out of the store.

But that was before he'd gotten a taste of Sunny's beef stew. Before she'd succeeded in stimulating his appetite. For food and, dammit, a whole lot more.

As he threw a bag of potatoes into the cart, Clint's mind was at war. The part of him that'd become a virtual recluse since Laura's murder knew that the smart thing to do was to send Sunny back to wherever the hell she came from.

Another part of him, a part he'd thought he'd buried with Laura, admitted that it was nice not having his house look like a toxic waste dump. And real food, after all this time, was definitely a plus.

The problem was, he considered grimly as he selected a plump roasting chicken, was that on the drive down the mountain, he'd spent too much time thinking about her wild blond hair and wide brown eyes. And dazzling smile designed to test any male's resolve.

"Clint!" A feminine voice shattered his unruly thoughts. "What a nice surprise, seeing you here."

He drew in a breath and slowly turned to meet Jessica Ingersoll's smile. "A man's gotta eat."

"Isn't that the truth. Ever since Rory and I began living together, my grocery budget has tripled." Her smile warmed at the mention of the man she'd recently become engaged to. "Speaking of eating," she said, a bit cautiously, Clint noticed, "we missed you at Thanksgiving."

"I was busy." Then, ashamed to be lying to this woman who cared about him, Clint exhaled a deep breath and explained, "I didn't exactly feel up to making party conversation."

"No one would have expected you to have to do that." She placed a hand on his arm. "Everyone there was your friend, Clint. And we're all worried about you. This is no time to be alone."

He thought it ironic that the woman whose job it had been to prosecute him had become a friend. Or at least she kept trying, even though he admittedly hadn't given her the slightest encouragement.

"I'm not exactly alone."

"Oh?" Her intelligent eyes swept over him and he watched as she catalogued the obvious differences in his appearance since the last time he'd come into Whiskey River, about three weeks ago.

"I seem to have hired a housekeeper."

"A housekeeper." She studied him again. "That's a good idea. I assume she's from around here? I remember Ida Littleton mentioning that she was thinking about going to work to help supplement Walter's social security check. At the time she'd said she was considering housework—"

"Actually, she's new in town." Not wanting to get into a discussion about something he didn't understand himself, Clint decided it was time to end the conversation. "Look, Jess, I'd love to talk, but I've got to get going, okay?"

"Of course." Although her quick smile was as warm as ever, he caught the tinge of concern in her eyes. Seeming not to care that she was a public official and that with the exception of the Branding Iron Café, this was the most public place in town, she went up on her toes and brushed a light kiss against his cheek. "Take care. And if there's anything you need—"

"I promise to call you." He flashed her a genuine, reassuring smile. It was the first time he'd really smiled since Laura's death and was mildly amazed when his face didn't crack.

Jessica seemed to be every bit as surprised by that smile as he was. "You really are looking much better. I'm so relieved."

Clint paid for his groceries, then stopped by Weatherby's Meat Locker to pick up some of the beef he kept there. It was only as he was driving back up the mountain that Clint remembered he'd forgotten to buy any whiskey.

Sunny was standing in the midst of soapsuds that covered the floor, when Clint entered the kitchen.

"Well at least the floor's going to be clean enough to eat off," he drawled as he waded through the soapy water to put the groceries on the table.

"Do you always choose such inopportune times to make a joke?" she asked with a hitch in her voice that told him she was close to tears.

Some deep-seated need to comfort made him run his palms over her slender shoulders. "I'm sorry."

"No. I'm the one who should apologize."

"For what?" He smoothed her hair, watching with absent fascination as it sprang back to life again the moment he took his hand away.

She lifted bleak eyes up to him. "Just look around you."

"Don't worry. I added flood coverage to my insurance policy last year." In her deep distress she missed the irony in his tone and took his words literally.

"It wasn't a flood," she mumbled, unable to meet his kind eyes.

"I know."

This time she thought she heard laughter in his voice. Certain she must be mistaken, she tilted her head back.

"I don't understand what happened. When Noel suggested I wash the dishes in the machine, instead of by hand, it seemed like such a good idea, but about ten minutes into the cycle, the dishwasher started belching all these soapsuds, and...well, everything just went downhill from there."

He glanced over at the bottle of liquid detergent on the counter, figured out what she'd done, and wondered how a professional housekeeper could have made such a rookie mistake.

But then he was distracted by a tear escaping her distressed brown eyes. As he flicked it away with thumb, he thought he'd never met a woman with skin so amazingly soft. "Noel was here?"

She swallowed hard against the still threatening tears. "With Tara Delaney. And Mariah."

"I suppose that explains the tree."

"Tree?" Sunny had completely forgotten the Christmas tree the women had brought.

"You know, that green thing leaning up against the house."

Sunny had come to the conclusion that she had no choice but to tell him the truth. Besides, she thought, Tara and Noel probably wouldn't give up easily. And if Clint discovered that she hadn't passed on the message, he might try to send her away.

Not that he'd succeed, she vowed. But it would be much easier to get about her business of finding him a new love if they were getting along.

"Yes, they brought the tree. And Tara invited us to dinner."

"Us?"

"Not as a couple," she hurried to assure him when she heard something akin to horror in his tone. "I'm sure the only reason I was included was because she's too polite to ask you to go alone, when it would mean leaving me here by myself during the holidays."

"She could have figured you'd welcome the time to spend with your family."

"I suppose that would be a possibility. If I had family."

"So you really are all alone in the world."

As desperate as she'd been feeling only moments ago, Sunny almost laughed at that. "Yes." She wondered what he'd say if she told him exactly how alone she was.

"You never said where you were from," he reminded her.

"Didn't I?"

Dammit, getting information from this woman was not a job for the fainthearted. "No."

"Well." She shook her head. "Imagine that." The little verbal thrust and parry made her feel better. Her equilibrium was returning and although soapsuds were melting all around her feet, she no longer felt like weeping. "I'd love to chat with you some more, Clint, but as you can see, I have a great deal of work to do, and—"

"You're not going to tell me, are you?"

"Would you believe me if I did?"

He considered that for a minute. "Probably not."

"Well then, I suppose you'll just have to trust me."

That was one option. The other option—the sane, sensible one—was, of course, just to send her away. But there was something about her that appealed to him. He was actually enjoying their little contest of wills.

"You know, if this were an old forties movie, you'd be Lana Turner about to poison my soup."

"Why on earth would I want to do that?"

He shrugged. "Because that's what mysterious femme fatales always do in old movies."

"You see me as a femme fatale?" Pleasure lit up her face.

"Sometimes." She really was quite lovely. Not in Laura's calm, classically beautiful way, of course. But she was definitely unique.

"How do you see me the rest of the time?"

He was about to shoot back that he viewed her as a pain in the butt, but something in those wide golden brown eyes told him that she'd dropped the game and was asking the question in earnest.

"I don't know." That was the absolute truth. "Why don't I think on it?"

"Good idea." Her smile was friendly, with no intimate overtones that might have set off warning bells. "And while you're thinking, why don't you think about this?"

He took the letter she pulled from her apron pocket and held out to him, scanned the few short lines and tossed it onto the counter.

"No way."

"But—"

"I am not going to that rodeo."

"Not even to defend your championship?"

"I don't give a damn about any championship."

There'd been a time when he had. A time when winning the bull-riding championship buckle was the high point of his day. Or, even the whole year. But that was before he'd discovered what true happiness was. It had also been before he'd learned, the hard way, how screwed up most people's values were.

It seemed that everyone Clint knew was always chasing after things—the biggest spread, a new pickup, a rodeo buckle. And although he'd never cared that much about money, Clint had to admit that the adulation of all those rodeo groupies had been a special perk of rodeoing. Most had been pretty, some had been downright spectacular, and all of them had been more than willing. Especially in those days when he was riding high on the circuit.

But none of them had been Laura.

Sunny tried again. "I don't want to argue, but—"

"Then don't."

His tone was so sharp she flinched. "Don't what?"

"Don't argue. I'm not going to Tombstone, Sunny. And that's it."

Frustrated, but loathe to show it, she nodded. "You're the boss."

His nod was brusque, his expression as grim as it had been when she'd first arrived. "And don't you forget it." That said, he walked out of the kitchen. He did not look back.

7

SINCE THIS WAS the first time he'd been absolutely sober in a very long while, Clint decided to tackle the books. He spent two hours in the den, moving numbers from one column of the computer spreadsheet to the other. Unfortunately, the bottom line didn't get any better. Despite the stabling business he'd started last year, the truth was he was in danger of losing the ranch. And, although only a few weeks ago he wouldn't have given a damn about that, today the idea stuck in his craw like a piece of tough beef.

Cattle prices were down, costs were up, and what little savings he had managed to sock away over the years had ended up going into the pockets of the Phoenix lawyer he'd been forced to hire after he'd been accused of Laura's murder. He hadn't really wanted an attorney, but since Matthew Swann had pulled every string in the state to make sure he was convicted, he hadn't had a whole lot of choice.

Although at the time he hadn't cared whether he lived or died, he sure as hell hadn't wanted the real murderer to get away. Which is exactly what would have happened if he'd been convicted.

He glanced over at the photograph on the desk. A young, stunningly beautiful Laura was smiling out of the frame as she had for so many years. The picture had been taken by the Las Vegas justice of the peace after their wedding.

The marriage had lasted less than a day. Matthew Swann had tracked them down and ordered his seventeen-year-old daughter to return home with him. Which, dammit, she had. Forsaking the vows she'd taken only hours before. Forsaking him.

It was only last year he'd discovered why she'd gone home with her father that long-ago day. Swann had threatened her in the one way guaranteed to ensure her compliance. He'd said if she didn't obey him, he'd have her new, nineteen-year-old groom arrested for statutory rape, which Clint had no doubt the man would have done. But even if he'd ended up serving jail time, once he'd been released, he and Laura could have been together.

After years of resenting her for turning her back on the life they could have had together, it had come as an unpleasant revelation to discover that she'd been trying to protect him.

Clint dragged his hands down his face. "So many damn years wasted," he muttered.

But that had been about to change. Because Laura had changed. No longer the submissive daughter, and tired of playing the role of the silent, acquiescent senatorial wife willing to turn a blind eye to her husband's infidelity, she'd come back to him determined to grasp happiness with both hands.

The months they'd spent together had been the most glorious and frustrating of Clint's life. Glorious because he was finally back in the arms of the woman he'd always loved. And he had loved her, dammit, even during those years when he'd tried to hate her. But they'd also been frustrating because of the way she'd kept putting off filing for divorce. Until it was too late.

He shook his head and desperately wished for a drink. There must be a bottle somewhere in the house. He was about to go look for one, when he decided that since he'd gone this long without whiskey, he might as well wait a little longer.

Saving the data, he closed the files and turned off the computer. Then he decided to see how Sunny was getting along in the kitchen.

The soapsuds were gone. The groceries he'd dumped on the table had been put away. And a chocolate cake with fudge frosting was on a plate on the counter. She was standing in front of the sink peeling potatoes. Although he fought against it, Clint found the domestic scene, not to mention the mouthwatering aroma coming from the oven, more than a little pleasant.

"Is that roast chicken?" he asked.

"With sausage dressing," she agreed. "I usually use wild rice, but you don't have any."

"You could have just wiggled your nose and conjured some up."

"I told you—"

"That's right, for some reason, your powers have been taken away."

"Because I wished it."

"Why the hell would you wish to lose your powers?"

"Well, of course I didn't wish for that to happen. But when you went out into that storm, I was worried about you, and was thinking if only I were a mortal woman, I could . . ."

Realizing what she'd been about to say, Sunny quickly closed her mouth. Color flooded into her cheeks. Once again, against his better judgement, Clint was intrigued.

"If you were a mortal woman," he coaxed, conveniently overlooking the fact that since there was no way in hell he was going to buy that fairy godmother story, he didn't believe she'd had any powers to begin with. "You could ... what?"

He was suddenly too close. And she was suddenly feeling too mortal. And vulnerable. "I don't think this is relevant ..."

"Sure it is." He touched her face, then traced a line from cheek to jaw. "If what you say is true, yesterday you were my fairy godmother. But now, since you've lost your powers, you're not."

His fingers cupped her chin while his thumb brushed against her tightly set lips. "Because of me." His eyes on hers, he lowered his head until his mouth was a breath away from hers. "I think, Sunny, that makes it very relevant."

She lifted a hand to his wrist, then, as something warm rose inside her, she found she lacked the strength to pull his hand away. "I don't understand." She was entranced by his low, utterly compelling voice. "I've never felt like this before."

"Like what?" He could see the reluctant desire rising in her eyes, could feel it in the heat beneath her skin, but some perverse instinct, some deep-seated need for control made him want to hear her say the words out loud. "How do you feel?"

"Shaky." Her tremulous voice confirmed that. She also wished his fingers hadn't brushed her neck. "As if I'm burning up from the inside out."

She tried to look away from his intensely probing gaze, but his eyes were holding hers with the sheer strength of his will. Never had Sunny felt so helpless. She swallowed as that skillful hand stroked her throat with a touch that started every nerve ending in her body tingling.

"Afraid," she admitted reluctantly.

"Aw, Sunny." His fingers continued their sensual assault across the slope of her breasts. "You don't have to feel afraid around me."

That said, he brushed his lips against hers. Lightly, but without a hint of hesitation. "You taste just like I've imagined."

"What have you imagined?" she whispered as her lips parted beneath his. The feel of his mouth on hers was the most intimate sensation Sunny had ever experienced. A dazzling, devastating dizziness washed over her.

"That you'd be delectable." He retreated briefly as if to assure her that he had no intention of plundering, then let his mouth touch hers again. "Delicious." And again. "Delightful."

He could feel her imminent surrender. Her body, which had been as stiff as cold steel when he'd first touched her began to heat. And soften. Her hands, which she'd pressed against his chest, as if to push him away, began to open and close, gathering up his sweater. Her eyelids had drifted closed, her lashes rested on her cheeks.

Clint knew that it wouldn't take much more to get her upstairs and into his bed. But as his own senses began to fog, he realized there was something strange about Sunny's kiss.

Other women—at least all the ones Clint had known over the years—would have responded in one of two ways: either by breaking off the kiss, or by kissing him back. But Sunny was doing neither. Instead, she was simply standing still, her fingers clutching his sweater, seemingly stunned by the touch of his mouth on hers.

Wanting to assure himself that he was just imagining this strange innocence, he pulled back and framed her face between his hands.

Sunny felt a distant twinge of regret as he took his
warm, clever mouth from hers. Murmuring a faint protest, she lifted her hands and linked her fingers together
around his neck. The unconscious gesture caused her
breasts to press against his chest, making Clint's inner fires
burn a little hotter. Flame a little higher.

"Open your eyes," he managed to whisper in a rough,
raspy voice even as he was wondering about the chances
of taking her right here atop the table to ease the ache inside him.

She did as he asked, but as he looked down into her eyes
and viewed the confusion shadowing the sherry-hued
depths, Clint cursed inwardly.

"You've never done this before, have you?"

Sunny knew she could never lie about this. "I've never
made love with a man, if that's what you're asking."

He was afraid of that. The only virgin he'd ever had in
his life had been Laura. But she'd been seventeen. At least
seven years younger than this woman.

"How the hell did a woman who looks like you—tastes
like you—manage to stay a virgin in this day and age?"

He didn't sound exactly thrilled by the news. Reminding herself that it didn't matter what he thought, because
he wasn't destined to end up with her, anyway, Sunny
tamped down her disappointment.

"I told you, I'm not mortal. At least, I wasn't until this
morning."

Lord, she was gorgeous, with her flushed cheeks and
wide gold eyes. But, unfortunately she was nuttier than a
heifer that had gotten into a dose of loco weed. That being the case, it would be unconscionable to seduce her.

Since her delusion seemed fairly harmless, Clint decided that the wisest thing—the kindest thing—would be
to play along.

"So, what you're saying is fairy godmothers don't have sex."

"Oh no!" The very idea was too impossible to even consider. "Physical touching is not normally part of our world."

"Doesn't sound like much of a world," Clint decided. "I suppose that goes for kissing, too?"

"Of course."

"Are you telling me that was your first kiss?"

She nodded, unconsciously touching her tingling lips where she imagined warmth—and Clint's dark, masculine taste—still lingered enticingly.

Her expression was guileless and direct and Clint would have sworn she was telling the truth. But he knew that was impossible. No woman who looked like her, smelled like her, could have possibly avoided being kissed. Unless she'd spent her life in some convent.

"So, how did I do?"

"Do?"

She really was sweet, he thought. "How was the kiss?"

"Oh." Her slow smile could have lit up all of Whiskey River for decades. "It was very nice."

"Nice?" He arched a brow. That's what he got for fishing for feminine compliments. A cold beer on a hot day was nice. A fire during a snowstorm was nice. The feel of the breeze while you were out on the lake trolling for trout was nice. "Perhaps I'll just have to try harder."

He was towering over her, looking too strong. Too male. Common sense, which admittedly had never been her strong point, warned her to back away. But fascinated by the muscle jerking in his cheek, and the heat in his blue eyes, Sunny couldn't have moved if her life had depended on it.

His head swooped down, and his mouth claimed hers with a force that sent twin lightning bolts of shock and pleasure ripping through her that scorched any thoughts of protest from her mind.

He tasted like coffee and smoke. He smelled like a northern forest, but as she drank in the crisp aroma of the pine soap he'd showered with, Sunny detected an underlying, evocative male musk that gave birth to a sudden, undefinable longing.

She was suddenly on fire. Flames leaped from a single spark, and burned their way through her veins. Smoke clouded her mind, sent her head spinning, closed her eyes.

His tongue thrust between her teeth, tangling with hers in an erotic dance that drew a low moan from deep in her throat. He ripped away the apron, and thrust his strong hand beneath her sweater, his touch creating heat and goose bumps in the small of her back as he pressed her against him.

He dragged his mouth away from hers, and down her throat, leaving a trail of sparks before the sharp nip of his teeth made her gasp his name.

Too fast. It was as if she'd been born of the fire that flared between them, as if she'd come to life in his arms. The potent flavor of her mouth was as intoxicating as whiskey. *Too hot.* He'd always prided himself on his control, but there was no cool control here. No restraint. It had been burned away by her taste, her touch, the scintillating little sounds she was making that only added fuel to the fire.

"Ah, Sunny," he groaned against her mouth, that sweet, succulent mouth, "come upstairs to bed with me." He bit her bottom lip, excited by the way her breath came rushing out from between those ravished lips. "I'll take you places you've never been. Wonderful, magical places—"

"No." Her mind spinning, her body turning to molten desire, Sunny had been on the verge of giving Clint anything he wanted. But it was that one word—*magic*—that managed to infiltrate her whirling senses. "Clint, I can't."

Clint cursed as the warm, hot woman he'd been about to ravish turned to stone in his arms. "Of course you can," he coaxed, not about to surrender yet.

She was the first woman in months who'd made him smile. The first woman who'd managed to rouse the sleeping sexual hunger he'd thought had deserted him forever. And, amazingly, she was the first person—male or female—who'd made him think that he just might live.

"I'll help you," he coaxed, his lips plucking tantalizingly at hers. All right, so he'd almost scared her off by coming on too strong. He'd back away a little and soon have her turned around again. "We'll be good together, Sunny. Just wait and see."

His lips promised worlds of wonder, his hands, as they skimmed over her body, causing a tingling from her breasts to that warm heavy place between her legs, invited her to give in. But Sunny knew that were she to surrender to this aching pleasure, she'd only end up hurting Clint in the long run.

Her assignment had been to find him his true love. Not to allow herself a dalliance, however thrilling it might be, with a man she'd soon be leaving.

No. As much as she longed to discover those magical worlds he could introduce her to, Sunny knew that the right thing—the only thing—to do would be to stop this now. Before it got completely out of hand.

"I'm not going to go to bed with you, Clint." She put both her hands against his shoulders and shoved, but she might as well have been trying to move one of the two-hundred-year-old ponderosa pine trees growing outside his house.

He lifted his head. Looking down, he saw both regret and determination on her lovely face.

"Fairy godmother, hell," he muttered. Although he'd released her the moment she'd made her intentions clear, unable to resist touching her, he skimmed his fingertips up her cheek. "You're a witch," he muttered. "Or a devil woman. Sent to torment me."

"That's not true!" She looked so honestly distressed, despite the painful throbbing in his loins, Clint was tempted to laugh. "I *am* your fairy godmother. And I'm here to rescue you, so if you'd only be a little patient, I'll find you the perfect woman and—"

"I'd just as soon have you."

His words shouldn't have caused such a rush of sheer feminine pleasure, but they did. Deciding the warm feeling must be one of the more attractive benefits of being mortal, Sunny tried to concentrate on the argument at hand.

"I'm not right for you."

"You felt pretty damn right a minute ago. When you were pressing against me so tight you could've been trying to crawl inside my skin."

She felt her cheeks flame at the embarrassing statement. It was, unfortunately, all too true. "I don't know what happened to me. I've never, ever, felt anything like that."

He could have told her that she wasn't the only one who felt staggered by what should have been merely a kiss, but decided to keep that little news flash to himself.

"It would have been good, Sunny," he said instead. His blue eyes swept over her, creating a renewed flare of heat. "Damn good."

"It would have been wrong," she insisted on a shaky little voice.

He laughed at that, then wondered why, although he was admittedly frustrated, he wasn't as angry as he might have been.

"Now we're back to Jiminy Cricket. If I'd wanted a conscience or a fairy godmother, for that matter, I would have run an ad in the *Rim Rock Record*."

"You insisted you didn't run an ad for a housekeeper, either," she reminded him. "But here I am."

"Yes." He shook his head. "Here you are."

Dammit, his voice sounded as unsteady as he felt. Even as he told himself that the out-of-control passion was nothing more than lust—the uncomplicated, biological desire of a male for a female—Clint couldn't remember ever being so rattled by the touch, the scent, the taste of a woman.

Never had needs flamed so high so fast. Never had Clint become so disoriented by a mere kiss. He hadn't meant for things to go so far. And he definitely hadn't meant to get as emotionally involved.

"I'm sorry."

"Sorry?" she echoed blankly, as if the word were unfamiliar, an expression from some archaic language.

"I didn't mean for things to get out of hand. I usually have better control."

"Are you saying that all kisses aren't like that?"

Her question, posed in that soft shimmering little voice, swept away his sexual hunger, along with his lingering discomfort. Clint threw back his head and laughed.

"Sweetheart, if all kisses were like that, people would burn up before they ever got to the good parts."

The good parts. Just the thought of there being more made Sunny's all too mortal blood hum in her human veins. For the first time she understood that all-consuming, ultimately fatal passion Antony and Cleopatra had shared.

The mood had effectively been shattered. And Clint decided it was for the best. Whatever was happening between them—and he refused to believe that crock about her being his fairy godmother—he needed time to think about the consequences.

His body was obviously trying to tell him that he needed a woman. Okay, maybe he did. Physically. But what he didn't need right now were any more complications in his life. And every instinct Clint possessed told him that this sweet-smelling woman with the luscious lips was a complication just waiting to happen.

"I've got some fence repairs to make that should take about an hour. What time's dinner?"

"Six. But I can hold it—"

"No. It'll be dark before then. I'll be back." The roast chicken aroma filling the kitchen was almost as enticing as her scent. "It's going to be nice to come back to a hot meal," he said, deciding he ought to give credit where credit was due. "I always used to do my own cooking. Before..."

His voice drifted off, but Sunny didn't need for him to finish the sentence. Before Laura had been killed, taking away his reasons for living. It seemed that everything in Clint's life would now be divided into the time before Laura's death, and the time after it. It was her job to make certain that his life after the tragedy would be filled with love and laughter.

Feeling a slight twinge of envy for the fortunate woman who would end up as Clint's wife, Sunny placed her hand on his arm. "It will get better."

Her touch, and her soft, sincere voice soothed like a cool creamy balm on a rope burn. Only a few days ago Clint wouldn't have believed her. He still didn't. But at least, back in some distant corner of his mind, he hoped that she was right.

WHEN CLINT RETURNED, twenty minutes early, Sunny was nowhere to be found. He looked upstairs, but the bedroom was empty. As was the bathroom. Finally, just when he began to wonder if she'd gotten discouraged and had taken off, he found her in the den, sitting in front of his computer screen.

"What the hell do you think you're doing?"

Sunny jumped at the rough, challenging voice coming from behind her. For a large man, he was certainly light on his feet.

"You scared me to death." She quickly tapped the exit key, then placed a hand against her wildly beating heart. "Do you realize that you have a very unnerving habit of sneaking up on people?"

"Only people I find breaking into my computer."

"Breaking in?" She arched a blond brow and attempted her most innocent look. "I don't know what you're talking about."

"It's quite simple." He crossed the room to the desk. "I leave you alone, expecting you to be busy with some domestic task—some *housekeeping* duty—but instead, I find you spelunking around in my computer files."

"I wasn't doing any such thing."

"Oh no?"

"Actually, I was just going to use it to write a letter."

"To whom? Your family?"

If he was trying to trip her up, he was going to have to do better than that. "I don't have a family. Remember, I told you that."

"I remember. But I can't quite recall whether that was before or after that bull about you being my fairy godmother."

The acid sarcasm stung. "Just because you don't believe me doesn't give you any right to be so nasty."

"And just because I'm stupid enough to let you stay here, doesn't give you any right to pry around in my business. You know, one of the first lessons my dad taught me was to learn where my business ended and someone else's started."

"I wasn't prying." When he didn't say anything, but just kept glaring down at her, looking hard and deep, she knew she'd met her match. "All right," she admitted. "Perhaps I was prying. But just a little. And with the very best of intentions."

"And those would be?"

"Well, you mentioned that you didn't make a great deal of money—"

"Actually, after last year, I'll be lucky to make a profit, so if you're thinking about doing a little computer magic to clean out my bank accounts—"

"I told you, I can't do magic."

"That's right. You lost your powers. I don't know why I keep forgetting that."

Sunny sighed. "I really do wish you'd make up your mind."

"About what?"

"Whether you want to yell at me, or make love to me."

"That's easy."

"Oh?"

"I want to do both. Yell at you." Feeling that unbidden pull, he leaned down and cupped her cheek in his palm. "And then I want to make love to you."

His touch stimulated those strange, edgy, wonderful feelings all over again. While he'd been out repairing the fence, Sunny had tried to convince herself that she'd imagined the way Clint had made her feel with those kisses. She'd hoped the feelings were merely fantasies of her newly mortal mind.

Unfortunately, the feel of his hand against her skin, warming and exciting at the same time, assured her that those feelings were all too real. How, she wondered, did mortals manage to get anything done when they were forced to spend their lives in such unnerving states of excitement?

"Don't you believe in a middle ground?"

"The middle ground's for people who don't know what they want."

"And you do?"

"You bet." When his thumb traced that now familiar sparkling warmth around her mouth, her lips parted instinctively to the provocative touch. "I want you."

And, heaven help her, she wanted him! Which was, of course, impossible. She hadn't been sent to earth to satisfy this man's sexual hunger, but to locate one very special woman—a soul mate who could soothe his pain and fill his life with the joy he'd been so cruelly cheated out of.

"What if I don't want you?" she managed to ask in a shaky whisper.

He smiled. "What if I don't believe you?"

"It's true." That was, she thought miserably, the biggest, most outrageous lie she'd ever told.

His smile didn't fade. If anything, it got wider. It was filled with a wicked sensuality that sent shivers through her. He leaned forward, and she found it hard to breathe.

"Why don't you kiss me again, then tell me that?"

He'd put his hands on either side of the desk; once again his mouth was unbearably close to hers. All either one of them would have to do would be to lean forward, just the slightest bit . . .

"I can't."

"I knew it." Masculine satisfaction practically oozed from every male pore. He leaned closer yet. The rich aromas of hay, leather and sweat surrounded her like a cloud, drugging her mind as she struggled to remind herself that what she was thinking was undoubtedly against every tenet of the fairy godmother's code of conduct.

"You don't understand."

"Sure I do."

He'd given the matter a great deal of thought while fixing that barbed wire. It was obvious that Sunny was like no other woman he'd ever met. As a rule, after his short marriage to Laura, Clint preferred his women experienced. In bed and out. They were women who knew the way the game was played, who took with the same enthusiasm they gave and didn't expect any rash declarations of love or marriage proposals the next morning. They were women who, for various reasons, had no more interest in happily ever after than he did.

Ranching was nothing like the romantic existence portrayed for decades by Hollywood. All right, he admitted, perhaps it was romantic, in its own way. Lord knows, he couldn't imagine doing anything else with his life.

But it was also hard, grueling work; long days, and nights often spent out on the hard cold ground while rounding up strays. The payoff was often not much more than the chance to work outdoors, surrounded by some of the most glorious scenery in the world and a feeling of satisfaction for a job well done.

Not many women were capable of understanding that, let alone appreciating it. Which is why he tended to stick to women who'd grown up on a ranch. Women like Laura.

"We haven't known each other all that long." He trailed his hand down her throat, enjoying the way her blood began to pound at his touch. "Your mama probably told you that nice girls don't go to bed with strangers."

His fingers slipped beneath the cowl neckline of her sweater. "And you've always tried to be a nice girl." There was no way he was going to believe she didn't want him. Not while her flesh was heating like warm satin beneath his fingertips. "But your mama's not here right now, sweetheart."

The warm seductive smile, which he hadn't had any occasion to use in months, had always been one of the most devastating weapons in his arsenal. "It's just you." He lowered his head slowly, giving her time to back away, but was not surprised when she didn't. "And me."

When his curved lips brushed hers, she exhaled a soft sigh of pleasure, and, he thought, invitation. "Whatever happens, I sure as hell won't tell." His tongue traced a wet hot circle around her mouth. "And I promise to respect you in the morning."

It was so tempting. And so wrong.

"I can't." Her words came out on a choked sound close to a sob. She shook her head and felt the mutinous moisture stinging at the back of her lids.

Clint was not inexperienced. He'd taken his first tumble in a hayloft when he was fifteen, with eighteen-year-old Becky Lee Miller, a long-legged barrel racer from Payson. He'd found riding soft, sweet-smelling Becky a helluva lot more fun than the broncs he'd been breaking on the rodeo circuit. And since he'd been a good-looking kid who won more than his share of buckles, he'd never lacked for female companionship. Which was why there was no way he could mistake the signs of Sunny's arousal.

Her pulse was beating like a rabbit's, her skin was fevered, her lips parted, just begging to be ravished, and her eyes were clouded with unmistakable desire not unlike Becky Lee's that long-ago sizzling hot Fourth of July afternoon. But Clint could not mistake the sheen of unshed tears in those dazzling gold eyes as well.

"If you're worried that I'd hurt you—"

"No." She clasped the rough, callused hand that was trailing up her cheek, turned her head and pressed her lips against his palm. The faint kiss sent a lightning bolt shooting from his palm to his groin, and Clint had to bite back a groan. "I know you wouldn't hurt me. But this isn't right. I'm not the right woman—"

"Now there you go again." Gathering up a fistful of her hair, he tilted her head back and flashed the woman-killer grin very few women were able to resist. "Talking foolishness again."

"Why can't we just be friends?" she pleaded. "The way you are with Noel, and Tara, and—"

"They're fine women," he agreed. "Nice women, and I'm proud to call them my friends. "But you've got to understand, Sunny, being just friends with a woman you want to love is a lot like having her invite you out behind the barn to look at stars, then just looking at the stars."

That said, and trying to ignore the little fact that he *needed* to taste those luscious lips again, Clint lowered his head.

FREE
LAS VEGAS
Game

GOOD FOR OVER £8.00 IN FREE GIFTS!

See inside →

PLAY FOR
FREE!
NO PURCHASE NECESSARY!

PLAY THE FREE
"LAS VEGAS"
GAME!

HOW TO PLAY:

1. Carefully pull away all three tabs on the right. Then check the chart below to see what is yours for FREE!

2. When you send back the card you will receive specially selected Mills & Boon Temptation® novels. These books are yours to keep absolutely free.

3. There's no catch. You're under no obligation to buy anything. And you don't have to make a minimum number of purchases – not even one!

4. The fact is, thousands of readers enjoy receiving books by mail from The Reader Service™. They like the convenience of home delivery... they like getting the best new novels at least a month before they're available in the shops... and they love their subscriber Newsletter packed with author news, competitions and much more.

5. We hope that after receiving your free books you'll want to remain a subscriber. But the choice is yours – to continue or cancel, anytime at all! So why not take us up on our invitation, with no risk of any kind. You'll be glad you did!

"LAS VEGAS" GAME!

OPEN HERE ▶

OPEN HERE ▶

OPEN HERE ▶

CLAIM CHART			
7	7	7	WORTH *FOUR* FREE Books and a *MYSTERY GIFT*
🍒	🍒	🍒	WORTH *FOUR* FREE Books
🔔	🔔	🔔	WORTH *THREE* FREE Books

YES! I have pulled away the three tabs. Please send me all the gifts for which I qualify. I understand that I am under no obligation to purchase any books, as explained on the opposite page. I am over 18 years of age.

T7JI

Ms / Mrs / Miss / Mr
_____

BLOCK CAPITALS PLEASE

Address
_____

_____

_____

Postcode

DETACH AND POST CARD TODAY!

The Reader Service™

FREEPOST
Croydon
Surrey
CR9 3WZ

NO
STAMP
NEEDED

8

THIS TIME SUNNY was quicker. And prepared. She pulled away, ignoring the pain at her scalp as the swift movement tugged her hair free. "We're not talking about love here, though, are we?"

There were lots of different kinds of love, most of which had little to do with what either of them were feeling. Clint knew he could lie, but he didn't.

"No," he said, meeting her regretful gaze with a steady one of his own. It was lust, pure and simple. But experience had taught him that lust was like a wildflower: it might not last long, but it sure was nice in the meantime.

Sunny waited for the relief she should have felt and was puzzled when it didn't come. "Well then, I'd say that settles that." She gave him the most remote smile he'd witnessed thus far, then walked out of the room.

When he heard her footfalls on the stairs going up to the bedroom, Clint cursed. Then he sat down to try to figure out what records the lady had been trying to access.

If she'd come here to steal from his bank account, she was flat out of luck. But why else, he wondered, clicking open the various files that contained almost his entire life, would she have been hacking away?

Frustrated, he stared at the screen and waited for the answer that was not forthcoming.

SUNNY WAS SITTING on the edge of the bed in the guest room, feeling strangely unsettled and more than a little discouraged when Andromeda suddenly appeared beside her.

"Things aren't going very well," the older woman said.

"Why don't you tell me something I don't know?" Sunny flopped back onto the mattress and stared bleakly at the ceiling. "It would be nice if the man would be the slightest bit cooperative."

Personally, Andromeda thought Clint Garvey was being wonderfully cooperative. It was obvious that he was intensely physically attracted to Sunny. Andromeda had been in the fairy godmother business long enough to know that for men, that was usually the starting place for a love match.

"You knew it wasn't going to be easy," she reminded Sunny.

"I know. But if I don't get him to that rodeo, I'm sunk."

"I think that may be an overstatement."

"He wants a woman," Sunny muttered. "And since I'm the only one handy right now, he thinks he wants me. I need to get him out where he can meet people. Mingle. And fall in love."

She rolled over onto her stomach and began distractedly smoothing the pillow case. "It would also be nice if he won the lottery. His financial situation is so precarious, I'm afraid he might not want to get seriously involved with another woman when he's so badly in debt."

"It's my understanding that being in debt is not unusual for the ranching business," Andromeda said. "He's an intelligent man. And a cautious businessman. He'll turn things around."

"Well, of course he will." Of that, Sunny had not a single doubt. "But there's no opportunity for him to make any money until spring." She sat up and hugged the pillow to her chest. "So, there's only one thing to do."

"And what's that?"

"I'm going to have to get him to that rodeo."

"And then?" Andromeda asked a bit anxiously.

"I'm going to fix him up with a rich woman."

"He doesn't appear to be a man who'd marry for money."

"No, he wouldn't," Sunny said. "So she's going to have to be sexy, as well." She pulled the flier out of her pocket. "Like this one." Looking at the amazing breasts packed into the sequined western blouse, Andromeda was amazed the rodeo queen could even sit on a horse without tipping horse and rider forward.

"I suppose that's what humans refer to as big hair," Andromeda murmured as she studied the froth of sable hair poofed out from beneath the straw Stetson.

"She has big everything," Sunny said. "Including a big bank account. Her family has owned land outside Whiskey River for generations. Lots and lots of land. And lots of cattle. They also hold several mining claims, and timber rights, and—"

"You've investigated her?"

"Of course. It was necessary, to ensure I found the right woman this time."

Andromeda rubbed her forehead. "I see. Then I take it you used one of your wishes to discover all this?"

"Oh, no. I used Clint's computer. I managed to access her banking records and her driver's license information, her birth certificate and school records, along with a record of childhood immunizations, her hair coloring formula and—"

"Gracious. That's a great deal of information."

"I seem to have a natural talent for hacking." Sunny's quick grin was filled with a very mortal pride. "If I'd only had a bit more time, I could have found out her shoe size."

"Imagine that." Obviously Harmony had been right about Sunny's skill for surviving in the mortal world.

"She's supposed to be a cinch to win the barrel racing event. And, since she and Clint had an affair a few years ago, it shouldn't take much to rekindle the spark. So, now all I have to do is figure out a way to get Clint to Tombstone."

Looking down at the photograph again, Andromeda felt a little twinge of concern. Harmony might be correct about Sunny being the perfect woman for Clint Garvey. Still, Andromeda wondered how many mortal men could resist such seductive packaging.

"I'm sure you'll figure out something, dear," she said absently as she wondered if Harmony had known about this complication.

"Of course I will," Sunny concurred firmly. Her chin was set, her eyes flashed with determination.

It should be a snap. She would figure out a way to get Clint to the rodeo, then stand back and let nature take its course.

Charmayne Hunter was the kind of woman men fantasized about. Clint wouldn't be able to resist. She wouldn't let him. She had to save one wish to get back home, but that left two she could use, if necessary, to ensure Clint married the right woman.

Once she'd succeeded, the board of administrators would have to acknowledge a job well done—perhaps they'd even name her fairy godmother of the month, which would propel her to senior status in the romance section—and restore her powers to her.

"It'll work," she said softly, not even noticing that Andromeda had left. "It has to."

SUNNY ALLOWED HERSELF a feeling of accomplishment as she watched Clint enjoy his dinner. He'd even opened the bottle of wine he'd purchased along with the groceries. Sunny had never tasted wine. There weren't any prohibitions against spirits, so far as she knew, but Andromeda had warned her that alcohol could cause a loss of control, and since Sunny's spells were a bit haphazard at the best of times, she'd never wanted to take the risk. However, since she no longer possessed the magic to cast any spells that could go wrong, Sunny decided to make an exception, just this once.

The wine tasted like a combination of silk and velvet on her tongue and warmed her going down. It also created a soft haze around her head that soothed her nerves which were usually tangled by close proximity to Clint.

"Do you know," she murmured, looking out the dining room window, "this is truly lovely country. I can see why you love it."

"Since it's pitch black out there and the moon's covered with clouds, I'm amazed you can see anything."

Accustomed to his sarcasm, Sunny was able to ignore it. "You know what I mean."

"Yes." His sardonic expression mellowed. "I do. There's something about the land," he murmured. "Something special. Something that gets deep in a man's bones and just doesn't let go."

When his quietly spoken words reminded her of his precarious financial straits, Sunny knew she was doing the right thing fixing him up with Charmayne Hunter. The cost of paying off Clint's debts was less than the price of the diamonds that had been sparkling like ice on the cowgirl's earlobes in that publicity photo.

"I guess most ranchers, and cowboys, feel that way," she murmured as he refilled their glasses.

"I suppose so."

As he poured the wine up to the rim, Clint remembered the old line he'd learned in high school about candy being dandy, but liquor being quicker. Getting her drunk might be some guys' solution to the perpetual hard-on he'd been suffering, but it wasn't his.

When he did make love to Sunny—and he had every intention of doing exactly that, in more ways than she could possibly imagine—he wanted to make damn sure she knew what she was doing. And with whom.

"I'd love to meet some."

"What?" He looked across at her, realizing that his mind had wandered as he'd pictured Sunny lying in a hayloft, her nude body warmed by a buttery yellow summer sun. Not that she was still going to be here come summer. But the fantasy was a pleasant one.

"Some cowboys," she said. "Did I mention that I've never been to a rodeo, and—"

"No."

"No?"

"No," he repeated firmly. "I'm not going to take part in any damn rodeo. Not this weekend. Not next weekend. Not next year. I'm done with all that."

"But the prize money could—"

"I said no." His words were bitten off, one at a time. His eyes, laced with warning, were hard and cold again. "What exactly is it about that word you don't understand?"

Frustrated because he'd ruined everything, just when they'd been getting along so well, Sunny polished off her wine and held out her glass for a refill.

"You've been cooped up here mush too long," she said, frowning a little as she heard the slur in her words. "It would be good for you, Clint." She was having trouble getting her tongue, which had become strangely heavy, around the words. "I do wish you'd reconsider."

One wish down. Two to go. As soon as she said the words, Sunny desperately wanted to call them back. She was about to wish she'd never said them in the first place, but stopped, just in time.

It did not take long. Clint became thoughtful as he took a long sip of his own wine. Sunny held her breath.

"Okay," he said finally.

"Okay, what?"

"Okay, I'll sign up."

Clint couldn't believe he'd just agreed to go to Tombstone with Sunny. And even as he wondered what the hell had gotten into him, he couldn't remember what his objections to the idea had been in the first place.

She was right, he decided. If he could successfully defend his championship, the prize money would go a long way toward keeping nim going until spring. Along with that incentive, he had to admit he liked the idea of showing off for Sunny. He'd hit it lucky enough times on the rodeo tour in the past to know that lots of women found going to bed with a cowboy a real turn-on. With any luck, Sunny would turn out to be one of those women.

"It's a long drive to Tombstone. We'll have to leave at first light in the morning."

"I'll be ready."

He shook his head as if wondering what he'd just agreed to. It would be all right, Sunny assured herself. So, she'd just used up a wish. She'd succeeded in getting Clint to agree to go to Tombstone. Surely the voluptuous cowgirl could take things from there.

Looking at him, her fingers practically itching to reach across the table and brush that dark shock of hair off his wide dark forehead, Sunny doubted that many women would be able to resist Clint Garvey. Heaven knows, it was proving difficult enough for her. And she wasn't even the one destined to be his love.

"SO," HARMONY MURMURED, "the plot thickens."

"I told you," Andromeda warned with a groan. "They're going to go to that rodeo and he's going to get involved with that silicone cowgirl and that'll be that."

"Clint's not stupid. If he'd wanted any kind of future with Charmayne Hunter he would have proposed to her years ago."

"What if Sunny makes a mistake and uses another wish?"

"That's out of our control. She has free will. We can nudge her in the right direction, we can give Clint a little push as well. We can set up a situation that should encourage their romance. But in the end, they have to make their own choices."

"I know." Andromeda frowned. "It's just so hard because . . ."

"It's Sunny."

"Yes." They both exchanged a look. They knew they shared a fondness for the well-meaning, yet distressingly untalented young fairy godmother. No words were needed.

THE MOOD BETWEEN them had changed. Clint felt the way his mare Buckskin always acted right before a thunderstorm—edgy and restless.

"I've got to go out to the tack room and get my gear together."

"Fine. I'll clean up here."

"Fine." Brilliant conversation you've got going here, Garvey, a nagging little voice in his head said. No wonder the lady's just dying to leap into your bed.

Frustrated by unruly emotions he'd thought he'd put safely away in the deep freeze, and wondering what made him think he and Sunny could get along cooped up in the front of his pickup for hours, he pushed away from the table, grabbed his jacket from the hook by the door and left the house.

Sunny stood in the window watching him walk toward the barn. The mercury light on the side of the house illuminated the driveway he was crossing and it occurred to her that for the first time since her arrival, he seemed to have a purpose.

"This will be good for him," she told herself. "It's just what he needs."

She knew she was on the very brink of turning Clint's life around. Although she didn't have a wish to waste on his winning the bull-riding event, she wasn't worried; he was fully capable of pulling that off by himself.

She would save a wish in case Charmayne might need a teeny nudge, but Sunny thought that was unlikely. After all, how many women wouldn't give anything to have a man like Clint in love with them?

The assignment, which she was now willing to admit had in the beginning looked hopeless, was now within reach.

So why, Sunny wondered, was she feeling so let down?

CLINT WOKE BEFORE dawn. His first thought was that something was wrong. He squinted into the dark purple shadows and tried to figure out what was making him feel so uneasy.

When the answer came, he had to laugh. He didn't have a hangover. The damn maniac running the drill press behind his eyes had taken his tools of torture and left for a more inviting host.

He sat up and ran his tongue along his teeth. His mouth no longer felt as if a badger had died inside it. And amazingly, for the first time in a very long while, he found himself actually looking forward to the day ahead.

He dressed quietly in the dark, so as not to wake Sunny who was still sleeping across the hall, then went outside to the barn to feed the horses. His own, and the ones he kept for a monthly stabling fee.

It was not easy to get away. After he'd made his decision to go to Tombstone last evening he'd called Mariah, who'd quickly assured him that she'd take care of things in his absence. She might be a famous Hollywood writer, with an Emmy on her mantle, but she'd grown up on a ranch and knew horses and cattle better than most of the men he'd worked with over the years.

She'd also let him know, in her forthright, no-holds-barred way, that she wasn't sure letting a complete stranger into his house was wise.

When he'd responded that he was a big boy, capable of taking care of himself, she'd suggested having her husband run a check on Sunny.

"Just to be sure she's not listed in the FBI files as some sort of crazed killer," she'd said.

"I don't think we have to worry about that, hon," he'd replied.

"I'm sure we don't," she'd answered in a tone that told him otherwise. "But if you'd just let Trace—"

"Mariah. Sweetheart." He'd sighed and reminded himself that this was the one other person who'd loved Laura as much as he had, despite the decade-long estrangement between the sisters. "You know as well as I do that would be a misuse of Trace's power. I'll be all right. Promise."

"Men," she'd huffed. "Dammit, Clint, you watch out for that woman. She's after something."

Clint had promised to keep an eye on Sunny.

"That's what worries me," Mariah'd answered dryly. "Don't forget, I've seen her. I'll have to admit she's stunning, in a rather fey sort of way."

As he'd hung up the phone Clint had wondered what she would have said if he'd brought up the fairy godmother story.

When he finished his work the sun was coming up over the tops of the pine trees, tinting the sky with brilliant fingers of pink and gold. He sat on a bale of hay outside the barn, smoked a cigarette and looked out over the land that bordered the Prescott spread.

Originally, the land had been settled by Ezra Prescott, Laura's and Mariah's great-great grandfather. Although most of the settlers on the Rim had gone back to the city when the army had been pulled out of the territory to fight in the Civil War, leaving the Apaches free to begin raiding again, Ezra had refused to budge. He'd passed the land down to his eldest son, Jake, who in turn had bequeathed it to his daughter, Ida, and Ida had shocked the entire county by leaving Clint a section of the sprawling ranch.

It was not the first time she'd shown Clint generosity. Years earlier, after Matthew Swann had fired him for eloping with his eldest daughter, Ida had offered him routine ranch work repairing fences, rounding up strays, building stock tanks.

"I hate to say this about my own flesh and blood, but my son can be a real jackass," the feisty old woman had told him after the ill-fated marriage. "And my grand-

daughter's a fool for letting her mule-headed father run her
life that way."

Although Clint had agreed, there hadn't been much he
could do about it. It wasn't until Ida died at the age of
ninety-eight that he'd discovered she'd carved him out a
part of the land she'd bequeathed to Laura. Which had
made them neighbors.

Not that they'd had much occasion to run into each
other, since Laura had spent most of her time in Washington with her senator husband.

Yet, there had been times, when he'd ridden along the
boundary line, and looked across Laura's land, that he'd
wondered if Ida hadn't been doing a little matchmak-
ing—hoping that if she threw the couple together, chemistry might win out over misplaced wifely loyalty and
daughterly devotion.

"It almost worked, Ida, old girl," he murmured, drawing in on the cigarette as he watched a pair of tassel-eared
squirrels playing hide-and-seek in the woodpile. "Laura
and I almost made it." At his feet, an orange-and-black
barn cat, basking in a pool of winter morning sunlight,
meowed, causing the squirrels to chase each other in cir-
cles up a nearby tree. "Unfortunately, close only counts in
horseshoes."

He put the cigarette out in the coffee can he used as an
ashtray. For the first time in a very long while, he had
things to do. Places to go. And people to see.

Like Sunny. Conveniently forgetting that the lady had
Complication written all over her, Clint was smiling as he
entered the house.

9

Sunny was pleased and grateful when Clint seemed to turn into a different person during the drive down the mountain toward the desert. He was more relaxed; more comfortable with her, and with himself. He even sang along to George Strait's "Easy Come, Easy Go."

"Lord, I love this land," he murmured, more to himself, she thought, than to her.

"It certainly is large," she agreed, looking around at the vast landscape. The soft early morning light of the December sun cast silvery stripes of light on the empty highway that disappeared beneath the truck tires as they drove south. "And lonely."

Clint shook his head. "Not lonely," he corrected. "Uncrowded. Sometimes, when you want to get away from things, you can ride out to a place so peaceful it's like crawling inside the quiet. Not everyone wants to live elbow to elbow."

Sunny couldn't imagine Clint living in the city. She suspected even Whiskey River might be a bit too settled for him. "I imagine that's easier for a man," she said, "than a woman."

She held her breath, hoping he'd validate her belief that he'd be better off with a wife accustomed to ranching. She'd already learned the hard way that matching an urban woman—who liked shopping, the theater and lunch with friends—with a man who preferred the quiet life in the country could prove disastrous.

"I suppose so." He shrugged. "That was one of the things about . . ." His voice drifted off.

"You know, it probably would be good for you to talk about her," Sunny suggested quietly.

He didn't answer for a long time. Sunny waited, content to watch the magnificent scenery flash by, the red-and-brown land with its dusting of early snow like a carpet unrolling in all directions.

"Laura loved this land," he said at length. Clint decided it was a milestone that he was able to say her name without choking. "She hated living in Washington, hated the artifice of politics. She was looking forward to coming home for good."

It was the first time, other than when he'd been questioned during the investigation, that he'd talked about her to anyone. Oh, he'd cursed her—a lot in the early days. But it hadn't taken long for his anger at her for leaving him to fade away, like one of the spectacular sunsets this land was famous for. The only problem was that once the anger had gone, there'd been nothing to put in that dark, gaping hole where his heart had once been.

"I can certainly understand why." Sunny caught sight of a herd of elk grazing in a meadow. As the truck approached, they all snapped their heads up in perfect synchronization and froze, seeming divided between alarm and curiosity. "It's magnificent," she murmured as the huge animals suddenly took off, bounding with amazing grace considering their size, into the woods

"The west is like a mistress," he said at length. "Seductive as all get-out, but uncontrollable as hell."

She thought about that for a moment. "Perhaps that's the seduction. The uncontrollability."

"I suppose you're right." Clint was surprised she could understand what was so difficult to put into words. "A control freak could never survive out here. Because you're hostage to your environment. You have to love ranching life for what it is, not what it should be.

"You can't make rain. You can't stop a late spring snow that freezes calves still wet from birthing, and you sure can't keep a hungry mountain lion from eating one of the new baby cows that does survive.

"But there's something about it that gets in your blood and won't let go. It's a way of life where living honorably with your neighbor—with all of creation—is a lot more important than the label stuck in your shirt or the bottom line on your tax return. Where a man can find peace. And perspective.

"And most of all, it's all about freedom. Adventure. Unlimited possibilities. The west is a place where a man, or a woman, is guaranteed something better. Something real."

His voice had roughened with emotion, making Clint feel like a damn fool. "Sorry," he muttered. "I guess I got carried away."

"Don't apologize." She smiled at him. "That was beautiful."

"I'm sure no writer. Or poet." And that's what it took to tell the story of this country he loved so much, Clint considered. A poet.

"But you care. And that's what's beautiful." She shook her head. "I didn't think people cared that way about the land, anymore. Not really."

He shrugged and wished for a cigarette, but didn't want to fill the cab of the truck with smoke that would cover up the sweet scent of flowers blooming on her skin.

"It's not that rare."

"Oh, I think it is," she argued mildly.

Just as Clint was a rare man. A good man. Sunny hoped that Charmayne Hunter deserved him. Because now that he'd allowed a glimpse of the man inside the wounded shell, she knew that she couldn't fix him up with just anyone in order to selfishly salvage her own career. There had to be a way, she assured herself, for them both to fulfill their dreams.

Silence settled over them again. The radio began to crackle. Clint leaned forward, twisted the dial, and located a station playing Reba McEntire.

"There's one thing you have to understand," he warned her as they approached Phoenix. "Rodeoing isn't a bunch of guys in ten-gallon hats playing cowboy. It's serious business. And it can be dangerous. I'm not going to have time to baby-sit you."

"I'm perfectly capable of taking care of myself."

"Yeah, you've done a real fine job so far," he muttered. "I guess you don't consider trying to turn yourself into a Popsicle anything to get concerned about?"

"Well, there was that," she admitted.

"And how about almost flooding my house?"

"I did not!" Her flare of temper fizzled as she noticed the laughter in his eyes. "I had everything under control."

"That's probably what Custer said, right before he rode into the valley of the Little Bighorn." His tone was gruff, but the faint light in his eyes gave him away.

"I knew it," Sunny said with satisfaction.

"Knew what?"

"I'm growing on you, aren't I?"

"Didn't your mama ever teach you it's not polite to dig for compliments?"

"No. I like compliments. Not that I get all that many," she admitted reluctantly, thinking of all the black marks in her fairy godmother record. "And you didn't answer my question. I am, aren't I? Growing on you."

He shrugged and felt the grin tugging at the corners of his mouth. "Yeah. I guess so. Kinda like a fungus on the side of a tree trunk."

Sunny could have been offended. However, since she understood he was joking, she smiled in response. And began humming along with the radio.

They stopped for breakfast in Tempe, and Sunny was not at all surprised when female heads turned to look at Clint as they walked into the Country Kitchen restaurant. He was definitely an arresting figure in his roper boots, his long legs encased in jeans, his broad shoulders stretching the seams of his blue chambray shirt and that fawn-colored Stetson that was obviously worn for work, not urban cowboy show.

They ate quickly, not bothering with conversation. Nor did they linger over coffee. Instead, Clint asked the waitress to fill his thermos and Sunny was not surprised when she expressed absolute delight at his request. From the way she'd been hovering over their table, refilling his cup as soon as he took even a sip, Sunny had the feeling that the woman—whose name tag read Brenda—would have been willing to do anything, no matter how personal, that Clint might ask.

The green of the mountains had long ago given way to the beige and pastels of the desert, which Sunny found every bit as stunning in their own way. She still couldn't get over the vastness of the land, the wide open spaces that seemed devoid of any life.

As they approached Tombstone—The Town Too Tough To Die, the Chamber of Commerce sign announced—they began to see more and more trucks on the road, many of them pulling trailers. Every so often one of the drivers would honk his horn and Clint would grin and wave back. Sunny began to realize that she was seeing another side of him, the easygoing rancher he'd been before the murder.

"I'll get us checked into the motel," he said as he passed the rodeo grounds.

The parking lot was filled with trucks and horse trailers and mobile homes. Men in jeans and brightly colored shirts moved among the vehicles, dogs trotting along beside them; a corral filled with horses had been set up on the perimeter, and columns of white smoke rose from somewhere in the midst of all the action.

"Then, while you settle into your room, I'll go sign up."

It was like nothing Sunny had ever seen; a wonderful, teeming world apart. As exotic as Jupiter or Mars. "Oh, can't I go with you?"

She was practically quivering with excitement, reminding Clint of Ginger, his old quarter horse waiting in the gate for the calf-roping event. That little mare had been the sweetest animal God had ever put on this earth, able to read his mind and do whatever he wanted a second before he thought of it himself. After she'd gotten too old to rodeo, he'd changed to saddle bronc riding because, although he'd never admit it to a living soul, leaving her behind and taking another horse would have made him feel as if he were betraying her.

"You realize, of course, that I've gotta be nuts," he said. He still couldn't figure out what had made him give in to Sunny's request in the first place.

"It's been my impression that most people are a little crazy. In their own way."

"You should know. Given your Looney Tunes fairy godmother story."

Sunny was disappointed that he still didn't believe her, yet encouraged by the humor in his tone. "You'll see," she promised. "One of these days you'll believe me."

"Sure I will." He stopped at a red light beside a truck loaded with bulls. Their wild brown eyes stared at her through the holes in the side of the truck's trailer. "The same day those bulls sprout wings and fly over the rodeo grounds like big live Macy's balloons."

"Oh, ye of little faith," she said absently as she stared back at the bulls. "Are those what you ride?"

"Yep. Them and the broncs."

"But they look so—" she shook her head "—big. And wild. And mean."

"That's the idea. Since bull riding is based on a scoring system, a cowboy is only as good as the bull is bad."

Something spooked one of the bulls. As they began shoving at each other, banging against the sides of the trailer and butting heads, Sunny began to doubt the wisdom of her plan. What if all she succeeded in doing was getting Clint killed? Then, she supposed, he'd be with his Laura. But that definitely hadn't been the plan.

Clint didn't have to be a mind reader to know what she was thinking. "Hey," he said, putting a finger beneath her chin and turning her gaze back to him. "It's going to be okay. I won't get hurt."

This was truly a terrible mistake. What on earth had she been thinking of? To think she'd wasted a wish on something that could end up getting him killed!

"You can't know that for certain."

"Sure I do."

The light changed to green. He crossed the intersection and pulled into the parking lot of the Boot Hill Motel. A neon boot at least ten feet tall blinked atop the roof. The sign said No Vacancy but Clint assured her that he'd managed to get the last two rooms.

"How?" she asked.

He surprised her by winking. "Because I'm the champ, remember?" He ruffled her hair. And then he dipped his head and kissed her, a brief, sweet kiss that ended too soon. "I'll be right back."

She watched as he went toward the motel office, noticing that even his walk was different. It was...cocky. A trio of women walking across the parking lot stopped when they caught sight of him. A bleached blonde with a frizzy perm called out his name and when he turned, threw herself into his arms. When she planted a long kiss right on his lips, those very same lips that had just finished kissing her, Sunny experienced a slow deep burn.

Clint laughed when the kiss ended, put his arm around the cowgirl's shoulders and the four of them entered the motel office together.

"I wanted him to get out and meet other women," Sunny reminded herself. "And, it seems that's exactly what he's doing. So, I should be happy, right?"

Right.

Now that he was getting back into the swing of things, it would be ever so much easier to match him up with Charmayne Hunter. But Sunny couldn't help thinking of that blonde's ripe red lips pressed so intimately against Clint's smiling ones, or remembering how his wide dark hands splayed on her waist had caused a strange, unaccountable emotion to seethe deep inside her.

It wasn't anger. Not exactly. It was too cold for fury, too focused for passion. She leaned her head against the back of the seat, closed her eyes and summoned up the vision again.

"Oh, no." As understanding sank in, Sunny groaned and covered her face with her hands. It couldn't be. She wouldn't let it be. But it was.

She was absolutely, unequivocally jealous.

She dragged her hands down her face and looked up at the bright blue desert sky. "Now what?" she asked.

HARMONY AND ANDROMEDA exchanged a look.

"Bingo," Harmony said with a satisfied smile.

"Granted, it's looking promising," Andromeda said. "But there's still that wild card Sunny threw into the game to deal with."

She pointed down at the bright pink truck hauling a matching trailer that was pulling into the lot. On the side of the trailer, in fancy gold script, had been painted Charmayne Hunter and Buttermilk. World Champion Barrel Racer.

The driver's door opened and long slender legs encased in a pair of skintight black jeans became visible. They were followed by the rest of Charmayne Hunter who did, unfortunately, look even better than she had in her publicity photo.

As the fairy godmothers watched, the rich, talented, sexy cowgirl Sunny had chosen for Clint took off her black hat, decorated with a gleaming silver band of turquoise studded conchos, and fluffed up her artfully tousled cloud of sable hair. Then, on a hip-swinging stride that drew a long wolf whistle from the driver of a passing pickup, she headed straight for the motel office.

"Why, Clint Garvey," the all-too-familiar voice rang out. "Fancy seein' you here."

Clint purposefully loosened his shoulders that had tensed instinctively when he'd heard Charmayne Hunter's voice. He took his credit card back from the motel manager and slowly turned around.

"Hello, Charmayne."

His gaze swept over her thick hair, her full lips, her magnificent breasts, which unfortunately felt like two huge stones, and her long long legs. He noticed that her cat green eyes hadn't lost their hardness in the time since they'd been together.

"You're looking as fine as ever," he said politely.

"Why, thank you, darling." Her smile was bright and pleased as she fluffed her hair and ran her tongue over those glossy red lips. "You're lookin' pretty good yourself." She treated him to a slow perusal, apparently liking what she saw. "A bit more rangy than you used to be. But on you, it looks good."

Thanks to Charmayne, the other women in the office were now all looking at him as if he were a breeding bull they were considering buying. Clint felt a warmth at the back of his neck and willed the flush to stay out of his face.

"Thanks. Well, I expect I'll see you over at the rodeo grounds. Meanwhile—"

Charmayne put a hand on his arm. Her nails were kept short, a requirement in her business, but they'd been painted a deep red hue the color of blood. "I didn't expect to see you here," she said, obviously not quite ready to let him go.

She hadn't been ready the last time, either. Clint remembered, with vivid clarity, the vase crashing against the doorjamb just as he'd walked through it.

"Tombstone's always been lucky for me. I figured I might as well give it a shot."

"You weren't at any of the summer rodeos."

"I was caught up in other things at the time."

"Yes, I read about that." Her crimson-tipped fingers stroked his forearm, her lips turned down in a regretful moue. But Clint, who had come to know this woman well, didn't miss the quick glitter of satisfaction in those hard green eyes. Her scent surrounded him like a suffocating cloud.

"I'm so sorry, Clint. I know how much you were hoping for things to work out with your Lana."

"Laura."

She arched a dark brow. "Excuse me?"

"Her name was Laura." He pried her fingers off his sleeve. "And as much as I'd love to stay here and shoot the breeze with you, Charmayne, I've got someone waiting out in the truck."

"Oh?" Her smile was quick and sly and wicked. "How nice that you've recovered from your bereavement."

Her words caused a familiar prick of guilt. "She's just a friend," he said, sounding too defensive even to his own ears.

The smile widened. "Everyone ought to have friends."

Leaning forward, she pressed her lips against his. The kiss was as clever and hot as he remembered, and included a lot of the tongue action that she'd always been so good at. And it moved not a single thing inside him.

Not wanting to create a scene in front of such a rapt audience, he took hold of her arms and gently, but firmly, moved her away from him.

"It's been good seeing you again, Charmayne." His tone said otherwise. "Perhaps we'll run into each other over the next couple of days."

Undeterred, she trailed a red-tipped finger down the front of his shirt. "Count on it, cowboy."

Feeling as if he were escaping the steel jaws of a mountain lion trap, Clint exhaled a huge breath of relief as he stepped outside the office.

"Was that Charmayne Hunter I saw going into the office?" Sunny asked when he returned to the truck. She'd been worrying about how to get the two of them together. Obviously, her luck was changing; with the two of them staying in such close quarters, there was no way he'd be able to resist the sexy appeal of his former lover.

"Yeah." He put the key in the ignition and shot her a curious look. "How do you know about her?"

"I believe I saw a flyer advertising her appearance here," she said, trying her best to sound vague. "It said something about her being a national champion."

"Several years running," Clint agreed.

"She's quite stunning."

"If you like that type, I guess." He twisted the key, bringing the engine to life. "Our rooms are on the second floor, around back."

"Oh, good. We'll have a view of the rodeo grounds."

"Yeah. Along with the aroma." Which would, he considered, probably not be as bad as Charmayne's perfume which seemed to be imbedded in his shirt. It overpowered Sunny's lighter scent.

"I don't care." Sunny could smell the oriental perfume clinging to Clint's clothes and hair and suspected that their reunion had gone precisely as planned. "I'm so excited about being here, I'd probably be happy sleeping in one of the barns."

He glanced over at her, viewed the truth of that statement in her sparkling eyes and shook his head. "You really are nuts."

His smile took the insult out of the words, and she smiled back. "You know," she said, thinking about her earlier realization that she'd broken the cardinal rule of fairy godmother prescribed behavior by letting herself become emotionally involved with her assignment, "you may just be right."

Her room was Spartan, but clean. The decor was an uninspiring cowboy motif. Since Sunny couldn't imagine anyone paying for such amateuristic depictions of old-time gunfighters, she concluded they must have been painted by the motel's owner. The carpet was orange, the bed-spread olive green with black stripes, the bed was lumpy, and the television was bolted to the dresser.

"They're not exactly five-star accommodations," Clint apologized as he carried her single bag into the room. "But the last time I was here the sheets were clean and the toilet didn't run all night."

"That's all anyone can ask," she murmured absently, tilting her head to try to figure out if Wyatt Earp really had three arms.

"The owner paints those," he said.

She nodded. "I thought that must be the case. Well, no one could ever call them derivative."

He laughed at that, oddly enjoying himself. Enjoying her. "Lord, you are an unrepentant optimist, aren't you, sweetheart?"

Before she could answer, they were interrupted by someone practically shouting his name from the door he'd left open.

"Clint Garvey," the female voice barked, "talk about a sight for sore eyes."

Clint spun around. "Dora, you dazzling female crea-ture, it's been too long." As Sunny watched in amaze-ment, he swept the sixty-something woman off her feet in a huge bear hug.

"You keep making time with my woman, and one of these days I'm gonna have to shoot you, Clint." This voice belonged to a short, stocky man who looked to be the same age as the woman. His head appeared bald beneath his mink brown Resitol hat, his belly overhung his belt and his legs were visibly bowed.

"It'd probably be worth it," Clint said, laughing as he lowered the woman back to the orange carpet. "Dora's one helluva woman, Rooster."

"You don't have to tell me that," the older man said. "I'm all the time havin' to chase away you young bucks."

"I can't help it if men find me fascinating," the woman said with a wink toward Sunny. She thrust out a hand. "Hi. I'm Dora O'Neal. And that jealous old coot over there is my husband Rooster. And you are . . . ?"

"Sunny." As Sunny's hand disappeared into Dora's larger one, she felt the calluses that spoke of a lifetime of hard physical work.

"Now, isn't that a nice name. And it suits you, too. With all that pretty sunshine-bright hair. I used to be a blonde. Remember Rooster?"

"I sure do. That was the summer I ended up in the Laramie jail because Jess Lawson took too much of a shine to you."

"He gave me a little peck on the cheek after we did the two-step. It wasn't nothing to get riled up about," she explained to Sunny.

"His hands were in the back pockets of your jeans and his mouth was getting damn close to yours," Rooster complained. "I had no choice but to throw him over the bar."

"You threw a man over a bar?" Sunny asked, appalled and fascinated at the same time.

"He was younger then," Dora answered for her husband. "I swear, that was forty-five years ago and the man is still bent out of shape over one little kiss."

"You'd have to be a man to understand, right, Clint?" Rooster appealed to Clint.

Clint laughed. "You're not going to get me in the middle of this one, Rooster. Think of me as Switzerland. I'm staying absolutely neutral."

"To think I can remember when you had guts," Rooster complained with a slow shake of his head. "What do you think, Sunny? Should a new bride let another man smooch her at her own wedding reception?"

"I believe it's traditional to kiss the bride," Sunny said.

"Ha!" Dora barked. "You see, you old goat! That's the exact same thing I told you forty-five years ago." She grinned at Sunny. "I think you and I are gonna become good friends, Sunny."

"I'd like that," Sunny said, conveniently overlooking the fact that once she got Clint matched up with Charmayne Hunter she'd be leaving Arizona forever.

"Women," Rooster complained. "Trust them to stick together. No offense meant, ma'am," he said to Sunny.

"No offense taken, Mr. O'Neal," she assured him with a smile.

"Thank you, ma'am." He smiled back, flashing tobacco stained teeth. "You signed in yet, Clint?"

"No. We just got here. I figured we'd head over to the rodeo grounds in a little while."

"Why don't you come with me? Since I'm currently out of work, I'll let you buy me a beer at the saloon next door."

"You're out of work? I thought you were working at the Forster spread in Montana."

"I was. But it got sold to one of them Hollywood movie stars who decided she wanted all the cattle sold off to make room for her emus."

"Her what?"

"Emus," Dora said. "You know, those big ostrichlike birds."

"I know what they are. Why on earth would anyone want to own any?"

"Why, didn't you know?" Rooster drawled sapiently. "Beef's out, cowboy. Now, emu steaks, that's the meat of the future."

"Not my future," Clint said decidedly.

"Mine neither. Which is why I turned down her offer to be head wrangler."

Clint threw back his head and laughed at that.

"What's so funny?" Rooster demanded.

"I was just picturing you riding on the back of one of those big birds."

"It's not a pretty vision," Dora agreed. "Which is why I didn't shoot him when he turned down the offer for more money in a week than we'd normally make in a year.... Why don't you boys go along and catch up on things? I'll help Sunny unpack."

"I don't have that much," Sunny demurred.

"That may be," Dora agreed. "But if we don't get rid of those two, we won't have any opportunity for a girl to girl chat."

Afraid that the chat would involve Dora fishing for information about her, Sunny didn't find that idea very encouraging.

"Will you be all right?" Clint asked.

She could sense that he wanted to go with Rooster. She also couldn't help noticing how relaxed he seemed with the older couple.

"I'll be fine," she assured him.

"Of course she will," Dora said. "Now you two go scoot. We've got some serious gossiping to get down to."

Just as Sunny had feared, Dora didn't waste any time. Clint had no sooner left than the older woman turned to her, hands splayed on her ample hips and said, "So, have you known Clint long?"

"Only a few days." Sunny opened up her suitcase, grateful that she'd thought to conjure up some clothing that first day. She had no idea what she would have done if she'd ended up without her powers or any clothes.

"Oh, I like those," Dora said, leaning over to pluck a pair of hot pink jeans from the suitcase. "And they go great with this shirt and vest!"

Sunny stared down in disbelief at the suitcase filled with colorful rodeo gear. She'd never owned anything like these clothes; she'd never *seen* anything like them. She looked at her suitcase once again to assure herself it was, indeed, the one she'd conjured up. Then she realized what had happened, and grinned.

ANDROMEDA GLANCED WITH surprise at Harmony. "I seem to recall you saying something about free will. And Sunny being on her own."

"Clothes aren't going to make Clint Garvey fall in love with her," Harmony countered. "And they're not going to make her realize that her future is with Clint. But they will let her dress appropriately. I wouldn't have let Cindy go to that ball without the proper gown and I won't have Sunny not looking her best this rodeo weekend."

"Those aren't exactly glass slippers," Andromeda observed as Sunny took the pair of pointy-toed rainbow-hued boots from the suitcase.

"Glass slippers would be inappropriate for a rodeo. And besides," Harmony said, "I like these better."

SUNNY LOVED THE boots. She ran her fingers over the overlay of brightly colored leather that depicted a vaguely familiar western scene.

"Well, I'll be dogged," Dora said as she looked closer at the boot. "That sure looks like that big old red rock that rises up behind Clint's house."

"Yes, it does, doesn't it?" Andromeda had definitely outdone herself this time, Sunny thought.

"I thought you'd only known Clint a few days."

"I have."

"So how did you get a picture of his ranch on your custom boots?"

"It's a coincidence," Sunny said. "I didn't even notice the resemblance until you pointed it out to me."

"Well, I'll bet that Clint notices it right off," Dora said. "That sunset is a real nice touch."

"Yes." Sunny smiled, thinking how surprised Clint would be when he saw the amazingly realistic leather portrait of his ranch. Maybe he'd finally believe her. "It is, isn't it?"

10

THE BAR WAS dim, cool, and crowded. Cowboys in stiffly starched jeans sat at the bar, the heels of their boots hooked over the rungs of wooden stools as they flirted with cowgirls dressed in everything from cotton to sequins. The cowgirls, none of whom appeared a bit shy, were happily flirting back.

All the tables were taken and in the center of the room, on a postage stamp-sized dance floor, a couple was twirling their way through the Texas Two-Step.

"So," Rooster said to Clint, "how are things holding up? Financewise?"

Clint shrugged. "They could be better." He took a long drink of his icy beer. "Then again, they could be worse."

"That's the ranchin' business." Rooster took a pull from his own bottle. "I'll bet Matthew Swann ain't hurtin' any."

Clint's jaw hardened. "I don't want to talk about Swann." Just thinking about the man who'd been his father-in-law for one brief day, gave Clint the urge to order a double shot of whiskey, but he reluctantly stuck to the beer.

"Sure. To tell you the truth, as tough as things are right now, I'm glad I'm not working for him anymore."

"You could be. If you hadn't stuck up for me last summer."

"Hell, the day I can't stand up for a friend is the day I'm six foot under with daisies growin' over me. Besides, the man was a real sumbitch."

"Can't argue with that." Clint took another drink.

"I may be poor these days, but at least I don't think Maalox is one of the major food groups anymore."

Clint laughed at that. "The man does have a way of clenching up your insides. So, what are you going to do now that you've turned down the golden opportunity to become an emu wrangler?"

"Don't know." It was Rooster's turn to shrug. "This is a bad time of year to find work. I was thinking Dora and me might head out to Texas or Oklahoma. Or, mebee Mexico."

"Mexican food always gave you heartburn," Clint said.

"Well, there is that," Rooster agreed. "But if you can't afford the tamales, you're not in much danger of gettin' heartburn."

True enough. "I wish like hell I could offer you something, Rooster, but—"

"Hell, boy—" Rooster slapped the younger man on the shoulder "—don't you worry about me. I've survived a lot worse than this." His grin faded and his mouth gaped as the door to the bar opened. "Hot damn," he said.

Clint looked up just as Sunny walked into the bar with Dora. She was dressed like a cowgirl in snug, creased jeans, a sunset-hued cotton western-cut blouse and cream Stetson. She'd pulled her hair back into a braid but errant strands had escaped, framing her exquisite face with gleaming gold. She looked born to the western clothes.

"Glory be," Rooster said, lowering the longneck bottle that had been on the way to his mouth. "If that ain't just about the prettiest filly I've seen in a lifetime of rodeoing." He shot a sideways look at Clint. "I told you last summer it was important to get back on a horse after you took a fall. Looks like you found yourself a champion."

"It's not what you're thinking."

It did not escape his notice that Sunny'd garnered the attention of everyone in the place. The men looked like mongrels drooling over a juicy rib eye steak; the women were decidedly less appreciative. As he watched one cowboy at the end of the L-shaped bar stand up and begin to saunter toward the women, Clint didn't know exactly why he was angry. But he damn well was.

Fortunately, before he had to warn the would-be suitor that the lady was taken, Dora spotted Clint and Rooster and the two women started walking across the bar toward them, leaving the cowboy with a dejected look on his face. *Tough*, Clint thought with a flare of male satisfaction.

"Sunny and I are hungry," Dora told the men without preamble. "We figured it might be a good idea for you two to treat us girls to some barbecue."

"I can't think of anything I'd rather do," Rooster said, sliding off the stool. "You sure look real pretty tonight, Sunny."

"Thank you." She dimpled prettily.

"Show Clint your boots, Sunny," Dora coaxed.

Sunny bent down and pulled up her jeans to reveal the top of one leather boot.

"Well, ain't that the niftiest thing," Rooster said. "Look at that, Clint. It's your place."

"It seems to be." Clint looked at her. "I don't suppose you'd care to tell me how you managed that."

She grinned up at him. "Magic."

As Rooster and Dora laughed, Clint continued to stare at her. His dark, thoughtful frown began making her nervous.

"If you don't want to go out—"

"Whatever Dora wants is fine with me." He finished off his beer, then put his hand on her waist in a proprietary

gesture. "You can't claim you've experienced a rodeo until you've had Kitty Campbell's barbecue beef. If heaven
had a taste, it'd be Kitty's barbecue."

"It's her secret sauce," Dora informed Sunny. "Passed
down from her great-grandpappy. People have been trying for years to figure out what's in it, but she won't tell.
There's a pool going. It costs a buck to enter and the first
person who guesses right wins the pot."

Always interested in new recipes, Sunny was looking
forward to tasting this alleged heavenly ambrosia. "How
much is in the pot?"

"Probably about five thousand dollars, give or take a
couple hundred," Rooster answered.

"Five thousand dollars?" Sunny stopped on her way
across the dirt parking lot.

"Like Dora said, a lot of people have tried to guess over
the years."

Five thousand dollars! Sunny's head was swimming as
they wove their way through the trucks and trailers to the
source of the billowing smoke that smelled of mesquite
and grilled beef. Thinking of all the things Clint could do
with so much money, she regretted her loss of powers even
more. She supposed she could use a wish. But that would
only leave her with one, which she needed to save just in
case Charmayne and Clint needed a little help getting together.

But if forced to use that last wish, she'd never be able to
go home. Which would leave her stuck here on earth,
without her powers, or the man she loved.

Loved? The thought reverberated through her mind,
bouncing around like one of the steel balls in the pinball
machine by the door of the Boot Hill Saloon.

She couldn't love Clint. Oh, she cared for him, certainly. After all, who wouldn't? Beneath his gruff exterior

was an honorable, caring man. And she certainly felt a great deal of compassion and sympathy for his loss, which again, was only natural.

But love? That was a solely mortal human concept. And she was . . . oh, dear heavens, Sunny thought. She *was* human. And if that wasn't bad enough, she'd fallen in love with her assignment. A man destined for another woman.

"Something wrong?"

Clint's deep voice managed to filter through her tumbling, whirling thoughts. "What?" she asked blankly staring up at him. At his rugged, weather-hewn face, at his startling crystal blue eyes, at those full hard lips whose dark mysterious taste she could imagine even now . . .

"The way your mouth's turned down, if you're not careful you're going to step on your lips," he said.

"Oh. I was thinking of something."

"I kind of figured that out for myself. So, want to let me in on whatever's got you looking like someone just ran over your favorite dog?"

Not on a bet. She let out a long breath. "I don't think so."

He'd half expected another of her irritatingly glib evasive answers. But instead of annoying him, she'd succeeded in piquing his curiosity. Who was Sunny, anyway? And what the hell did she want from him?

Every woman wanted something. Most of the ones he went out with just wanted a good time, some wanted the money they thought he had because he owned a ranch, and still others had confessed they found the idea of going to bed with a man arrested for murder exciting.

Even Laura had wanted him to help her escape a miserable marriage. Oh, he had not a single doubt that she'd loved him. But the need had always been there, hovering in the background, even if he hadn't ever wanted to face it. To talk about it.

But Sunny was different. For the life of him, he couldn't figure out what her racket was. She had to be up to something; there were too many gaps in her story. It was almost as if she were hiding from someone.

"Are you married?" he asked suddenly, as the possible answer to her secretive behavior flashed into his mind.

"Married?" The way he'd been looking down at her, hard and deep, had tangled her nerves all over again. Of all the uncomfortable questions she'd been expecting, that definitely hadn't been one of them. "Of course not! If I were married, I never would have let you kiss me."

Although he knew it was a mistake, he couldn't resist skimming a finger along the curve of her jaw. "You kissed me back," he reminded her.

His low, tantalizing voice sent a hundred—a thousand—chords strumming inside her. She stood looking up at him, her eyes on his, wishing she had the strength to back away.

"Yes, I did. Which I wouldn't have done if I'd pledged myself to another man."

Her expression was so grave, Clint was tempted to laugh at her naiveté. He almost told her that such old-fashioned virtue was out of place in this modern world of instant self-gratification, drive-through wedding parlors and no-fault divorces.

He wanted to drag her back to the motel and show her exactly what she was missing, all the hot and heavy mind-blowing sex she insisted on depriving them both of. But he couldn't do it. Because, as weird as it was, he found himself almost admiring her reluctance to compromise her own outdated beliefs.

"Okay, so you're not married. Maybe you're running away from a convent?"

She tensed as he began playing with the dangling turquoise-and-silver earring she'd found in her suitcase. "Do I look like a nun?"

He skimmed a glance down her body. The blouse was studded with pearlized snaps that would make taking it off her a breeze. The snug jeans might be a bit difficult to drag down those slender legs, but that would be half the fun. And then, after he'd dispensed with them, he could kiss his way back up again. . . .

Damn. Hunger rose, hot and insistent, once again urging him to take her somewhere dark and private where he could kiss her senseless.

"No." He shook his head and jerked himself back from the rocky precipice of temptation. "You don't look like any nun I've ever seen."

"That's because—"

"I know. You're my fairy godmother." Shaking his head, he linked his fingers in hers and resumed walking. "I gotta say this for you, sweetheart, once you pick a story, you damn well stick to it."

The barbecue beef was everything Dora and Rooster had promised. Tart enough to jangle the taste buds, tender enough to melt on the tongue. As Sunny sat on the bench beside Clint and across from the older couple, she chewed the succulent meat and decided that there were probably far worse fates than spending the rest of her life being mortal.

"Well," Dora demanded, "what do you think?"

"It's truly wonderful."

"A slice of heaven, right?"

"Absolutely." And a little bit of Kentucky. "What do you have to do to guess the recipe?"

"Simple. You give Kitty a dollar and take your best shot."

"Why wouldn't she lie?" From what Sunny'd witnessed, when it came to money, most mortals were less than honest.

"Because she wouldn't," Dora insisted.

She was so emphatic, Sunny believed her. She turned to Clint. "Would you mind advancing me a dollar on my salary?"

He was sorry he hadn't thought to ask her if she'd needed any money. "Sure." He lifted his hips off the bench. As she watched his hand go into his pocket, pulling his jeans tight against his groin, Sunny suffered a weakening jolt of need so strong she was relieved she was sitting down.

"Here." He peeled some twenties from the roll and handed them out to her.

"One is enough." She plucked a single twenty from the bills, slid out from behind the table and headed off toward the cooking wagon.

Dora, Rooster and Clint exchanged a look, then followed.

"Hi," Sunny greeted the cook, whose weathered face was red from the heat. And, Sunny suspected, a bit of her great-grandpappy's recipe.

"Back for seconds are you?" Kitty asked cheerfully. "Good idea. You're a pretty little thing, but a tad too skinny. Men like women to have a little flesh on their bones."

She patted her own ample hips that were straining the seams of her indigo jeans. "Something to hold on to in bed." She grinned up at Clint, who'd come up behind Sunny. "Ain't that right, cowboy?"

"Whatever you say, Kitty," he drawled.

"Actually, I've come to make a guess," Sunny said. "About your barbecue recipe."

"Oh, really?" Kitty's laugh was rich and bold and suggested she'd just gotten herself another sucker. "Hey everyone," she called out. "There's a little gal over here wants to make a guess."

That was all it took to bring people to their feet and begin hurrying toward Kitty's wagon. Sunny glanced with surprise at Dora.

"Everybody around these parts has already run out of guesses," the older woman explained. "It's kinda a treat to get some new blood in the contest."

Kitty's eyes narrowed as she studied Sunny, as if looking at her through the sights of a gun. "You're not from around here."

"No." That was definitely an understatement.

Kitty's hands were still on her hips, but now they appeared to challenge. "How many times have you even eaten barbecue?"

"This is my first time."

There was a knowing mumble among the crowd. Even Clint had to shake his head at her audacity. But she was kind of cute, he had to admit, standing there with her chin stuck out, facing down Kitty, who'd once spent sixty days in jail for throwing a meat cleaver at her cheating third husband.

"This is your first time. But you think you can figure out what people—folk who know good barbecue when they taste it—have been trying to figure out for near a quarter of a century?"

Sunny refused to be intimidated. "I believe I can, yes," she said mildly.

"This is gonna be like takin' candy from a baby." Kitty laughed, a rough, heavy smoker's bark as she plucked the twenty-dollar bill from Sunny's fingers and counted out a ten, a five, and four ones in return. Meanwhile, more money began changing hands in the audience.

Everyone watched as the cook took a big slotted spoon, stuck it into the stainless steel vat and pulled out some shredded beef covered with a brick red sauce.

"Want another taste? Just to refresh your tastebuds?"

Sunny ignored the mockery as she'd ignored the laughter. "Thank you for offering. But that's not necessary."

"Well then." Kitty dropped the spoon and folded her beefy arms across her chest. "What's the secret ingredient?"

"Moonshine."

There was a roar of laughter from the spectators, laughter that gradually dwindled as people realized that Kitty was not smiling. Instead, her face had gone as white as the paper napkins on the counter as she stared in disbelief at Sunny. Red splotches marred those too pale cheeks.

"How the hell did you know that?" she asked finally.

"I've spent some time in Kentucky," Sunny said. "I once just about went blind taking a sip of Hatfield moonshine." She decided there was no point in trying to explain about her relationship to Devil Anse Hatfield.

"My great-grandpappy was a Hatfield," Kitty said. "That's where I got my recipe."

Sunny smiled. "Isn't it a small world?"

"I STILL CAN'T believe it," Clint said later that evening as they walked back to the motel. He was carrying the huge jar stuffed with dollar bills. "How the hell did you know that?"

"I told Kitty the truth. I spent some time in Kentucky. Once you've tasted mountain moonshine, you don't forget it."

"Apparently not.... So," he said with a casualness he was a long way from feeling, "were you working in Kentucky?"

"Yes."

"As a housekeeper?"

"No."

She sighed, wishing he hadn't brought it up. She'd been feeling so good about the money, although she still hadn't figured out a way to get him to take it. Perhaps she'd just leave it behind when she left to go home.

When that thought proved too depressing, she turned her thoughts back to the subject at hand, where once again she'd gotten herself stuck in a no-win situation.

If she told the truth, Clint undoubtedly wouldn't believe her. And even if he *did* believe her, how encouraged would he be about his own impending match when he discovered that she was partly, albeit accidently, responsible for one of the most famous family feuds in America?

"You know," he suggested as the silence lingered, "we can play twenty questions all night. Or you can just tell me."

"All right." She shivered. Although the day had been warm, the night was cool, making her wish she'd worn a jacket. "I was Devil Anse Hatfield's fairy godmother."

He cursed beneath his breath, and juggled the money jar as he shrugged out of his denim jacket in order to put it around her shoulders. "I should have seen that one coming."

Sunny caught hold of the lapels and drew them together, cocooning herself in the jacket's warmth. "You should have."

"Guess you kinda blew that romantic love match." His tone was as mild as hers had been.

"I suppose you could say that." Not wanting to think about her previous failures, she turned her gaze upward and drank in the sight of the millions of sparkling stars. "It's so beautiful," she said softly. "The sky is as wide as this land. And so clear it's as if you could see forever."

"And beyond." In a casual gesture that felt comfortably right, he put his arm around her shoulder and stood with her, looking up at the vast black sky studded with diamonds.

Music from the saloon was filtering into the parking lot, a sad song about a cowboy missing the woman he'd loved. The sound of a woman's laughter reached them on the cool night breeze. Across the street at the rodeo grounds, horses whinnied and radios set to different country stations clashed discordantly.

But all distractions faded slowly away as they stood, side by side, drinking in the beauty of a clear December desert night and the unspoken enjoyment of each other's company.

Sunny felt as fragile as fine crystal beneath his arm, Clint thought, yet the way she'd stood up to his boorish behavior proved that she was definitely no pushover. Escaped strands of hair drifted like silk over his hand and her scent, which he knew he'd be able to recognize blindfolded, teased his mind, tormented his senses, and tempted his resolve to stay out of any emotional quicksand. If it were only that easy.

Sunny knew she was playing with fire, being out here, alone in the dark with a man who could make her nerves jangle with merely a sideways glance and cloud her senses with only a kiss. The thing she should do, she told herself, was move away now. Take her money jar and escape into her motel room, then bolt the door behind her. Which would keep Clint out of her room. But unfortunately, it was too late for locking him out of her heart.

She nearly wished for her own fairy godmother to set things right, then just in time, snapped her mind shut. The second wish was for Clint. The third was to return home. So long as she kept that in mind, Sunny assured herself, everything would work out just fine.

"Five thousand dollars for your thoughts," he murmured.

She glanced up at him, puzzled, then remembered the money he was holding. "I thought the saying was a penny."

"Gotta figure in inflation." Unable to resist, he brushed his lips against the top of her head, breathed in her scent and wondered what the hell they were doing standing in a public parking lot when they could be in his room, in his bed, tangling the patched sheets. "And, you've got to consider the lady who's thinking those thoughts." His breath fanned her temple. "You're definitely no cut-rate lady."

His words, as warm as the breath that was heating her skin, made Sunny feel as if she were about to melt into a little puddle at his boots.

"I was thinking how complicated life could be," she answered softly, afraid to look up at his face for fear of what she'd see.

"It doesn't have to be." His arm tightened, not forcefully, but enough to press her tight against him. "The way we're both feeling right now—the way this has been building from the beginning—we could go to my room, or yours, if you'd feel more comfortable, take our clothes off and drive each other crazy."

"Well that's certainly romantic," she muttered. His body was as hard as the rocky escarpment of the Mogollon Rim country he called home and just the thought of him pressed against her, holding her, claiming her, sent a renewed, painfully familiar thrumming through her veins.

"I suppose I could fancy it up with pretty words." He nibbled at her earlobe, then made her shiver when he touched the tip of his tongue to that sensitive spot he'd discovered behind her ear. "But it wouldn't change what's happening here."

"And what's that?" As his lips continued their sensual teasing, she closed her eyes, and still saw stars.

"Attraction." He kissed her left eyelid and made her sigh. "Chemistry." A sound like a whimper escaped her parted lips as he moved to the right lid. "Animal magnetism." He skimmed a finger down her nose, then kissed the slightly tilted tip.

"Sex, desire, the man-woman thing." He touched his mouth to hers, a touch as gentle as a feather, then, when she leaned toward him, pulled just out of reach. "We'd be good together, Sunny."

He looked down at her. Moonlight danced on her exquisite, uplifted face and he felt something inside him move. Something he feared had nothing to do with chemistry. And everything to do with much deeper feelings.

"However," he said, snapping himself out of the spell he'd begun to weave around her, around himself, "I understand how all this might be new to you. You need time to mull things over. Time to get used to the idea that you and I are a perfect match."

Although it took a major effort, Sunny opened her eyes and forced herself to look directly into his. "You're wrong."

He surprised her by grinning at that. An amazingly boyish grin that held considerable charm. "What kind of fairy godmother argues all the time?" he asked. "I thought you were supposed to grant my every wish."

"I told you, that's—"

"Yeah, yeah, a genie. But there must be some bylaw somewhere that states you're supposed to make my every dream come true."

"Of course, but—"

"I figured as much." He nodded, pleased with himself as he began walking up the outside stairs. With his arm looped casually around her waist, she had no choice but to go along.

"How about handing it over?" he asked when they reached her door.

"What?" Shocked, she looked up at him. He couldn't mean . . . No, Sunny assured herself, he wouldn't mean *that*. "The key, darlin'." He chuckled and held out his free hand.

Grateful that the light over the door had burned out, which kept him from seeing the embarrassed color that had flooded into her cheeks, Sunny dug the key out of her suede bag and handed it to him.

He opened the door, then, when she was inside, handed her the jar of dollar bills that was heavier than she would have guessed.

"And by the way, just for the record, you know what I said about dreams?"

"Yes?" She tensed, waiting for him to laugh and tell her he was only joking about beginning to believe her.

"I've been dreaming of you." That said, he bent his head and took her lips.

He took his time, kissing her with tenderness and finesse. His tongue tangled with hers, his teeth nibbled at her lower lip, drawing her into the mists. With her arms wrapped around the jar, she was quite literally helpless. Unable to resist his seduction, and her own rising needs.

"Clint . . ." His name came shuddering out between her tingling lips on a soft moan. Every nerve ending in her body was tightly coiled waiting for something she couldn't quite understand.

"Darlin', you were wrong." He dipped his tongue into the slight hollow beneath her bottom lip and discovered an erogenous zone she would never have imagined existed.

"About what?" Was the room spinning? Or was she?

"About losing your powers. Because we're definitely dealing with something otherworldly here, Sunny." He touched his lips to hers again, once, twice, a third time; each light kiss lingering a heartbeat longer than the previous one. "Something that feels a whole lot like magic."

His entire body ached. His head throbbed and Clint knew that if he didn't leave right now, he was lost. Of course, he thought with grim humor, he was probably lost anyway. But when he fell, he wanted to make damn sure he didn't take that long fatal tumble alone.

"Good night, sweetheart." He backed away, enjoying the desire in her eyes. Then, because he couldn't resist the lure of those softly parted lips, he reached out and skimmed a finger around them, and was rewarded by her tremor. "You'll dream of me."

As he would dream of her. As he had since she'd first arrived. Hot, sexy, raunchy dreams that left him as randy as an old billy goat.

Sunny stood looking up at him, unable to answer. Unable to think.

Satisfied and frustrated at the same time, Clint gave her one last smile, then pushed her gently back into the room.

"Make sure you double bolt this door behind me," he said. "This isn't the safest neighborhood in town."

Sunny's mind was reeling as she watched the door close, cutting him off from her.

"Lock the door, Sunny," he called to her.

Moving as if on autopilot, she stuffed the money jar under one arm and managed to do as instructed.

"That's the girl. Sweet dreams, darlin'."

He was whistling as he walked the few feet to his own door, leaving Sunny all alone, confused and wanting.

11

THE PIQUANT AROMA of Kitty's moonshine-enhanced barbecue mingled with the scents of straw and manure. Cowboys wearing fancy competition chaps over their best jeans leaned against fences and watched the action.

One cowboy sat atop a hay bale, chewing tobacco as he stared off into space, presumably making his upcoming eight-second ride over and over again in his mind. Others rubbed mink oil into their saddles, practiced their rope throws, polished their belt buckles one last time, or found a quiet corner away from the action to pray.

Little girls rode imaginary horses between the trailers. Little boys, wearing too-large hats that rested on their stuck-out ears strutted behind the scenes, twirling child-size ropes, dreaming of the day they'd compete as their fathers were doing today, and as their granddaddies had before that.

Wives and girlfriends sat on fences and in the bleachers. They drank from bottles of beer and cans of Pepsi, wet from ice chests, and balanced paper plates of barbecue on their laps while trying to keep track of their children, who, as children will always do at rodeos, tried to sneak away to see the horses.

A country band, brought in from Tucson, entertained the crowd with renditions of old favorites like Garth Brooks's "Rodeo" and Billy Dean's "You Don't Count the Cost."

Sunny was captivated by all the exotic sights and sounds.

"This is so wonderful!" she told Dora as she watched the Grand Entry. The dazzling performance by the precision equestrian drill team caused a flurry of camera shutters all around the arena.

"I've lived sixty-six years and still haven't found anything that compares," the older woman agreed with a broad smile.

The oversize American flag drew cheers from the audience as they stood up to sing the national anthem. Cowboys, even those preparing to compete, stopped and held their hats over their hearts. Sunny found the sight one of the most moving things she'd ever seen.

The day flew by. There were bareback riders, saddle bronc riders, calf ropers, men who wrestled steers, women who rode their horses around barrels with blinding speed, and clowns who not only entertained, but risked their lives to keep contestants alive by drawing the attention of angry bulls from fallen riders.

Although it wasn't necessary, the bass-voiced announcer kept the audience's enthusiasm up by encouraging them to applaud the losers as well as the contenders, "because that's all that cowboy's gonna go home with today, folks."

Sunny's heart was in her throat as she watched Clint climb the chute and settle astride the muscled back of a tall dark horse named Desperado. The instant he felt the unwanted weight, the bronc begun bucking wildly, making the cowboys who'd been standing on the gate scatter.

"I can't stand this," she moaned, covering her face with her hands. But, unable to resist looking, she reluctantly splayed her fingers. "I just know he's going to get killed."

Earlier in the day a young Navajo bareback rider from Window Rock had made a one-point landing right on top of his head. A worried hush had come over the arena as the paramedics had taken him out on a stretcher. Although the announcer later informed the crowd that the cowboy was going to be okay, Sunny knew that the outcome could have been tragic.

"Clint knows what he's doing," Dora assured her. "Don't you worry, he'll make his eight seconds just fine."

"But it says here in the program that Desperado is one of the wildest horses there is. That no one's been able to ride him all year."

"That's in Clint's favor. The whole thing's scored on points, honey. It doesn't matter how much ability and grit you have if you don't get a good bucking horse. Clint was lucky drawing that outlaw."

Luck, Sunny decided, definitely meant something different when it came to rodeoing. She watched in horror as the bucking horse rammed Clint's elbow against the metal rail. Seconds later, the gate opened and the still-scrambling horse tore out of the chute like an explosion of dynamite.

The next eight seconds were the longest of Sunny's life. The wildly bucking black horse did everything it could to throw Clint to the dirt, and Clint did everything he could to stay on Desperado's back. She watched with a fierce and anxious intensity, and vaguely heard Dora explaining that Clint must keep one arm in the air and his spurs pointed toward the horse's head, a position that made the furious horse only buck harder.

Finally, just when Sunny thought her nerves couldn't take it any longer, the horn sounded, signaling the end of the ride. She felt every muscle in her body loosen as the pickup rider helped Clint off the bronc's back and onto the ground.

"A ninety-six," Dora said, nodding with satisfaction as the announcer read the score. "So long as he stays on tomorrow night, nobody's gonna beat that."

Sunny didn't care about points. She was just vastly relieved that he'd survived. Concerned about his arm the horse had jammed into the rail, she left the bleachers, and went behind the scenes to make certain he was truly all right.

She found him, engaged in what appeared to be an intimate conversation with Charmayne Hunter. The woman's hand was on his cheek; her hungry eyes were practically eating him up. If Clint had been one of Kitty's barbecue beef sandwiches, Sunny thought with a burst of irritation, he'd be a goner.

Reminding herself that having chosen this woman for Clint, she should be relieved they seemed to be hitting it off so well, Sunny was about to retreat to the bleachers when Clint caught sight of her.

Saying something Sunny couldn't hear to Charmayne—what she would have given for lip reading abilities just then!—he called Sunny's name and began striding toward her, his fringed chaps making his legs look even longer and more muscular.

"So," he said, grinning down at her, "what did you think?"

"Before or after I had my heart attack?"

He laughed at that, feeling more carefree than he had in a very long time. "Watching rodeo isn't for the faint-hearted," he agreed.

"Forget about watching. How about doing?"

"Ah, that's the easy part because you're so busy trying not to be embarrassed by landing on your ass, you don't have time to be scared."

She shook her head but found herself enjoying the laughter in his gaze. Lines she'd never noticed before crinkled upward from the corners of those vivid blue eyes.

"I'd be lying if I said my nerves aren't gnawing in my gut when I climb into that chute," he admitted. "But that's what rodeo's all about. Giving the bronc or bull every opportunity to beat you. Then showing him he's not tough enough to do it."

"You realize, of course, the fact that you even consider riding an angry animal that outweighs you by at least a thousand pounds proves you're crazy."

"Ah, but that's the beauty of it." His grin was quick and warm and definitely contagious.

"I'm afraid the logic of that escapes me," she said dryly, even as she smiled back.

"I'm crazy." He bent his head and brushed his curved lips against hers. "And you're crazy." His mouth lingered, creating a flare of heat that went all the way down to her toes. "Which I'd say makes us a perfect match."

"I keep telling you—"

"Yeah, yeah, I know." He lifted his head and looked down at her. "You're the wrong woman for me."

"I am."

"And I keep telling you, you're wrong about that, sunshine. And before this weekend is over, I'm going to prove it to you."

"That's not possible." She might have been wrong about Cleopatra and Antony. And the Hatfield-McCoy match had definitely been a mistake, as was the Prince of Wales and the shy young teacher. But Sunny had chosen carefully this time, using logic—and a computer—rather than her heart.

"Of course it's possible." He took hold of her hand and laced their fingers together. "Don't forget, you're talking to the only man to ride Desperado to the buzzer this year." Point made, he began walking across the field.

"Where are we going?"

"To the medical tent."

"The medical tent?" Suddenly she remembered her reason for tracking him down in the first place. "Oh no," she cried out as she noticed the bright red stain darkening his black-and-white patterned shirt. "You did hurt yourself."

"Nothing that a few stitches won't fix," he assured her. "But I figure it might be a good idea to get it sewed up before the bull-riding competition. Old Frankenstein's already mean enough. No point in giving him a whiff of fresh blood."

"Frankenstein?" Her voice rose as she felt her own blood leaving her face. "You drew a bull named Frankenstein?"

"Yep. He's a real outlaw." The grin Clint flashed her was as cocky as hell. "Lucky, huh?"

To Sunny's vast relief, Clint got through the bull riding without a scratch, and once again earned the highest score. However, she was not looking forward to the next day when she'd have to watch him practically lying on his back on two thousand pounds of potential killer on the hoof all over again. She'd already been forced to watch in horror as one bull had gored a hapless cowboy from Utah in the side.

But she wasn't going to worry about that. Not now. Wanting to enjoy this one stolen night with the man she loved, she'd accompanied Clint, Dora and Rooster to the Boot Hill Saloon, where everyone had gathered to either drown their failure, or celebrate success. The cowboys had showered, shaved and changed into clothes that didn't smell of horse, dust and sweat and although a lot of the women were still dressed in jeans, others had switched to fringed denim or broomstick-pleated skirts that swirled around their legs as they danced the Cotton-eyed Joe.

"Now this is the life," Rooster said, as he tipped back his wooden chair and observed the couples out on the dance floor. "A day at the rodeo, followed by a little drinkin', a little dancin', later some lovin'—"

"You're pretty sure of yourself, cowboy," Dora challenged with a toss of her head.

"Now sweetie pie," he countered, "that's not true at all. But I'm damn sure of you."

She punched him playfully in the arm. "You keep talkin' like that and I'm gonna find me some young stud to ride off into the sunset with."

Rooster looked less than terrified by that threat. "Wouldn't do you any good."

"You don't think I could get one of them cowboys?" Her feigned glare was sharp enough to slice the neck off his beer bottle. "Some men like a woman who knows what she's doin'."

"All men like a woman who knows what she's doin'," Rooster agreed in that slow drawl that had endeared him to Sunny. "And I've not a doubt in the world that if you announced you were available, you'd have more young bucks buzzing around you than bees at a honeycomb.

"However," he concluded, "the reason it wouldn't do you any good is because I'd come after you. And bring you home where you belong. With an old, out-of-work cowboy who wouldn't have any reason to get up in the morning if you weren't there."

"Dammit, Rooster O'Neal," Dora complained. "If you keep talking like that, I'm going to turn into a blubbering fool."

He leaned forward and brushed a tear away with a gentle touch that made Sunny's own eyes fill. "Just thought I ought to tell you how I felt," he said. "It dawned on me today, that with all the troubles we've been having, I've been a bit snappish lately—"

"Like a horse with a burr under the saddle," Dora said with another sniff.

"Exactly. So I decided I'd better start making amends before you up and left me."

"Not on your life, you old goat." She reached out and put her hand on his grizzled cheek. "You're stuck with me. Because in my book, cowboy, for better or worse means for good."

"We've sure had a bunch of the worse lately," he muttered.

"Which means we're bound to get to the better real soon."

Clint and Sunny exchanged a look that told her they were thinking the same thing. That as bad as their financial situation might be, Dora and Rooster O'Neal were two very lucky people.

"How about a dance?" Clint said suddenly, wanting to give the couple some privacy.

"I don't know..." Although she appreciated what he was trying to do, she'd been watching the complicated line dance and doubted she could follow along.

"Don't let us embarrass you," Rooster said. "Sometimes, even when you're married, you've got to remind yourselves of your priorities. But I guess you'll both find that out for yourselves, some day."

Sunny wasn't about to respond to that comment. "May I ask a question?" she said instead.

Rooster signaled the waitress for another round. "Sure."

"I was watching a late movie on the television in my room last night—"

"Had trouble sleepin' did you?" Dora asked sympathetically.

"Just a bit." Sunny steadfastly ignored Clint's knowing look. "Anyway, it was about some men from the city who went to this ranch to take part in a cattle drive—"

"*City Slickers*," Dora said.

"That's the one." Sunny nodded.

"Jack Palance stole that movie," Rooster said. "Lock, stock and barrel."

"I don't know," Dora mused. "That Billy Crystal was awfully cute. And it was real sweet when he delivered that calf."

"Nothing sweet about delivering a wet bloody calf," Rooster argued. "And what was that about, taking the dang thing home with him?" He shot a look at Clint. "You ever hear of anyone takin' a cow to New York City?"

"Not one that wasn't already cut into New York strip steaks," Clint said.

"The thing I was wondering," Sunny began again, determined to make her point, "is if that's possible."

Rooster stared at her. "Taking a cow to the city? We already told you—"

"No, I was talking about the cattle drive. Is it possible to actually get people to pay you to do your ranch work?"

"Sure," Rooster replied. "More and more ranches are getting into that. It's kind of a spin-off of the old dude ranches, where city folk used to like to hang out and watch cowboys work.

"But after a while it seemed just watching wasn't good enough. These days, all sorts of people—doctors, stockbrokers, insurance men—actually get a kick out of saddle sores, sleepin' on the ground listening to coyote parties and trying to wrangle dumb surging masses of bovine stupidity."

"The movie certainly made it look appealing," Sunny said. "So, I was wondering—" she turned to Clint "—why you can't do that with your ranch?"

He looked absolutely horrified. "How about because I don't have any desire to baby-sit a bunch of whining greenhorns? That was a movie, Sunny. Not real life."

"But Rooster said—"

"I don't care what Rooster said." He put the bottle down on the table with a decisive thump. "I run a working ranch. I don't have any time for coddling pampered stockbrokers and prima donna movie stars. If I wanted to be in the vacation resort business, I'd plant a bunch of grass in the back pasture, learn how to caddy and open up a golf course."

"You know," Rooster mused, rubbing the gray stubble on his chin, "that's not such a bad idea."

"What the hell have you been drinking?" Clint shot an incredulous look across the table at his long-time friend. "It's a nutty idea."

"Lots of folks are getting into the business," Rooster said. "It's better than losing the ranch."

"Or turning it into an emu pasture," Dora said. "Clint, I think you should at least give Sunny's idea some thought."

"No way." He folded his arms. "Besides, an operation like that would take someone experienced with cows who also had a knack for handling people. And none of the seasonal hands I hire fit that category."

"Rooster does," Sunny said. She wasn't surprised that Clint hadn't liked her suggestion. She hadn't thought he would, which was why she'd chosen her time carefully.

The older man shot her a grin. "I was wondering if you were going to think of that. Or if I was going to have to nominate myself."

Clint's eyes narrowed and Sunny could practically see the wheels turning inside his head. "Then there's the financial problems," he insisted. "It figures that you'd have to have insurance, in case some fancy-pants urologist broke an arm when he got thrown off his horse, or a buffed-up soap opera star who wanted to play cowboy got his foot stepped on by a stupid cow.

"And then there's the logistics of trying to figure out if you were actually making a profit at the end of the day, after you'd added all those extra expenses, like cots and tents and food and—"

"You could have someone work out a financial plan," Sunny said.

"Accountants cost money. They're like lawyers. The last one I had to hire to straighten out some tax problems cost more than my vet."

"I'd do it for free."

"You?" He arched a brow. "I seem to recall hiring a housekeeper. I don't remember you saying anything about being a CPA."

"Well, I'm not, exactly. But I do have a talent for business management—"

"I thought your talent was cooking."

"My money skills are just as good. In fact," she said, meeting his challenging look with a level one of her own, "they're better."

"Well, imagine that," Rooster said. "Pretty as a new colt and brains, too. You'd better latch on to this one, Clint. Before she gets away."

Clint gave Sunny another of those long probing looks she was beginning to get used to. "I think you and I ought to have a little talk," he said finally.

She flashed him her sweetest smile. "Whatever you want."

Clint shook his head in frustration. "A smart woman like yourself should knew better than to give a man an opening like that."

His remark earned a hoot from Rooster, a laugh from Dora and made Sunny blush. Before she could come up with an appropriate answer, a young man she vaguely recognized came up to the table. His face, which she guessed, under normal conditions would have been handsome, was badly swollen; what parts weren't black or blue were a dark purple.

"Ah, Clint?" He was obviously uncomfortable. His hands were jammed into his back pockets, and he was looking down at the floor and rubbing a path in the sawdust with the toe of his boot.

"What can I do for you, Rope?"

"Well, I was wondering if I could talk to you in private, for a minute. If you aren't doin' anything too important."

"Well, I gotta tell you, Rope," Clint drawled, "under most circumstances, I'd probably have to shoot any man who interrupted just when I was about to dance with my lady."

The young cowboy shot a apologetic look Sunny's way. "Sorry ma'am," he mumbled.

"Don't think anything of it . . . Rope, was it?" Sunny replied.

"Uh, yes, ma'am. That's right. My daddy said he named me that hoping I'd grow up to be smarter than him and be a calf roper 'stead of a bull rider."

"Didn't see you doing much riding today," Rooster crowed with a laugh. "But you did a right fine job of flying, son. Although I wouldn't recommend landing on your pretty face next time."

Color flushed upward from Rope's collar, as bright red as the stripes in his American flag shirt. "Well, Clint, I'm sorry to have disturbed you, so—"

"Aw, jeez, Rope," Clint said, "can't you tell when your leg's bein' pulled?" He pushed his chair away from the table and stood up. "I won't be long," he told Sunny. Then, just in case there was any question about whose woman she was, he caught her chin in his long fingers, and kissed her so quickly that it was over before she had time to react.

"Poor Rope," Dora said as the two men walked out the door. "The way he's limpin' he's gonna be too stiff to climb up on that bull tomorrow."

Sunny suddenly remembered why the cowboy looked familiar; he'd ridden before Clint and had hit the ground right after the bull left the chute. She'd been terrified that he was going to get stomped to death. Fortunately, the clowns had leaped into action, and had successfully distracted the huge animal.

"I can't understand why anyone in his right mind would want to do this," she muttered.

"There's probably a good argument about cowboys not bein' in their right minds to begin with," Rooster allowed. "But in the beginning, it was a way for them to hone the skills they needed on the range. It was natural that things would get a little competitive."

"A little?" She'd watched a bareback rider compete with a broken wrist, complete with heavy cast.

"You know what the Duke said," Rooster answered with a shrug. "A man's gotta do what a man's gotta do."

Personally, Sunny thought that was about the most stupid reason for risking your life she'd ever heard. "The Duke?"

"You don't know who the Duke is?" Rooster looked at her with the same amazed disbelief he might have shown had Sunny suddenly announced that the bartender should get rid of the beer and start serving a nice dry California chardonnay.

"John Wayne," Dora said. "He was before your time, honey."

"She still should have heard of him," Rooster grumbled.

"Maybe the girl's got better things to do than sit around and watch old movies. Like figuring out a way to save Clint's ranch and get you working again."

"Yeah." He looked sheepish. "I'm sorry, Sunny. No offense meant. And, that's a right fine idea you came up with."

"Thank you, Rooster. No offense taken." She glanced over at the door and wondered what business Rope had with Clint. "I wish Clint thought so."

"He'll come around," Dora assured her.

"Can't imagine any male with blood flowing in his veins bein' able to keep saying no to you, Sunny," Rooster said.

Since she sincerely liked the man, Sunny wasn't offended by his chauvinistic statement.

"When Rooster's right, he's right," Dora affirmed. "You're just going to have to keep after him."

Sunny was about to answer that that was exactly what she intended to do, when the door opened again and Clint came back into the room. But before he could get to her table, he was sidetracked by Charmayne.

"Will you look at that girl," Dora complained. "She's got more brass than Sousa's band."

Sunny watched as Charmayne took Clint by the hand and practically dragged him out on to the dance floor. "She certainly can ride well," Sunny murmured, knowing that she was in deep, deep trouble when the sight of Charmayne pressing up against Clint created a physical pain in her chest.

This was what she'd wanted, she reminded herself. What Clint needed. But it was so hard. She sighed, thinking that being mortal could be both exhilarating and depressing at the same time.

"You don't have to worry about Charmayne," Dora assured her. "Whatever she and Clint had was over a long time ago."

"The girl's yesterday's box score," Rooster added.

"She'd be a good match for Clint, though," Sunny suggested. "They have so much in common, and she could help finance the ranch, and—"

"Clint's a grown man, Sunny," Rooster said. "And a bright one. Seems to me if he thought Charmayne Hunter was so right for him, he would have gotten hitched to her a long time ago."

"I suppose the fact that he was in love with Laura Swann had something to do with that," Sunny murmured, thinking that Charmayne couldn't get any closer to Clint unless she crawled inside his shirt.

"Sometime's it's tough gettin' over your first romance," Dora told her. "But a smart girl would rather be a man's last love than his first." She patted Sunny's hand.

"But I'm not—"

"It's as plain as the nose on both your faces," Dora said, cutting her off. "And Rooster and I think it's just dandy."

"Haven't seen Clint looking so loose in years," Rooster observed.

Sunny had to ask. "Not even when he was with Laura?"

"Laura was a lovely woman," Dora said. "Intelligent, pretty, sweet. But from what we could tell from watching that affair from the sidelines, Clint had more heartache than happiness where she was concerned. Even before she was killed."

Dora patted Sunny's hand. "Anyone can tell that you're good for him, Sunny,"

"But I'm not—"

"Don't you worry, most men are a little slow on the uptake," Dora interrupted again before Sunny could explain that she wasn't the right woman for Clint.

"Even if it takes more than one throw to land a steer and tie him, he's still roped and tied," Rooster advised knowingly.

"I don't understand—"

"What Rooster's tryin' to say is that you've got to keep trying."

"All you have to do to win," the older man said, "is get up one more time than you fall."

"That's enough with the cowboyisms, Rooster O'Neal. You're starting to sound like Gabby Hayes."

Although she had no idea of who Gabby Hayes was, Sunny laughed. Her stress somewhat relieved, she returned her attention to the dance floor. Although the song had ended, Charmayne and Clint were still standing in the middle of the floor, talking.

"They certainly look good together," she said pensively. No one could say that she hadn't made an attractive match.

Dora snorted at that. "Lookin' good has always been important to Charmayne. But like most people who are all wrapped up in themselves, she makes a pretty puny package."

"Girl doesn't have a whole lot of depth," Rooster agreed. "But she does fill out a pair of jeans right nice."

Unfortunately, she filled out everything right nice, Sunny thought. She was comparing her own slender body with Charmayne's voluptuous one as the woman tossed her head, then spun away from Clint, grabbed Rope, who was passing by, and began dancing with the young cowboy.

Sunny's rebellious heart skipped a beat as Clint sat down beside her, his leg brushing against hers. "I was going to ask you to dance," he said. "But I thought you might like to wait for a slow one."

"It looked to me as if you already had a partner." Sunny cringed as she realized exactly how uncharacteristically petty she sounded.

Dora gave a muffled laugh; Rooster whistled softly; Clint arched a dark brow as he leaned back and looked at her.

"What did Rope want?" Rooster asked.

"He and some other cowboys want me to give them bull riding lessons." Clint didn't take his eyes from Sunny's face.

"You gonna do it?"

"Might as well. Considering what they're willing to pay."

"Good idea, trainin' the competition," Rooster muttered.

"I figured out today, during that eight seconds, that I was getting too old to keep getting every bone in my body jounced around," Clint said absently, still looking at Sunny.

"Come on." He took her hand and stood up, pulling her to her feet. "'Night, Dora. Rooster. We've had a real good time, but it's gettin' late and Sunny's had a long day. We'll see you in the morning."

"Bright and early for the Jaycee's pancake breakfast," Rooster agreed with a grin.

As the couple watched Clint and Sunny leave the bar, Dora turned to her husband. "What do you figure the chances are of those two makin' that breakfast?"

"Slim to none," he answered, and seemed vastly pleased by the notion.

12

"WOULD YOU MIND telling me where we're going?" Sunny asked as Clint practically dragged her across the bar parking lot.

"I told you, I feel like dancing."

"The band's back in there."

"The dance floor's too crowded."

"I suppose that's why Charmayne had to dance so close."

He laughed. "Anyone ever tell you that you're real cute when you're jealous, sunshine?"

"I'm not jealous. Just observant."

"Whatever you say, darlin'," Clint agreed as they walked around to the back of the motel. "I'm not about to argue with you, not tonight."

She'd expected him to suggest they go to her room, but instead, he stopped in front of his truck and dug the keys out of his pocket.

"Now what?"

"Just be a little patient." He turned on the radio and punched the buttons until he came to a romantic Vince Gill ballad. "There we go." He turned and took her into his arms. "Now, isn't this nice?"

Even though she knew she was flirting with danger, she couldn't deny that it was wonderful. The night was getting chilly, but she felt radiantly warm. The sky was as clear as it had been the evening before, and overhead a full moon hung in the sky like a shiny silver dollar.

"It's very nice." Better than nice. Sunny thought it was the closest thing to heaven anyone could ever find on earth.

As Clint pulled her closer, Sunny turned her cheek against the front of his shirt. Their thighs brushed. He pulled her still closer. His hand moved up her back and tangled in her hair.

"Sunshine, you smell good." He pressed his lips against the top of her hair as they continued to sway to the music. "I've been meaning to ask you, what's the name of that perfume?" He had every intention of stopping by a department store in Phoenix on their way back to Whiskey River and buying a lifetime supply.

"I'm not wearing any perfume," she murmured as she felt her body melting against his.

He missed a step, recovered, then tilted his head back so he could look down at her. "You're not?"

Even in the dark, she could see the flame in his eyes, a flame that was scorching her skin. Her mouth was suddenly unbearably dry. When she unconsciously licked her lips, Sunny watched the fire flare higher.

"No." It was a whisper, barely heard despite the stillness of the night.

He shook his head, his expression one of male resignation. "You realize what this means, of course."

"What?"

"That we're in deep trouble here, Sunny."

She swallowed. "I know."

Without taking his eyes from hers, he ran his hand back down her hair, down to her waist. "I want to make love to you tonight. But I want you to want it, too."

What was wrong with her? She lifted a hand to her spinning head. "I do, but—"

"No." He pressed his fingers against her lips. "No buts. I don't want to hear any bullshit about how you're the wrong woman for me. I've had my share of women, Sunny, and believe me, I know what I'm saying when I say I've never wanted any of those women as badly as I want you tonight."

He hesitated as if expecting her to continue to argue, not knowing that she couldn't have uttered a single word if her life had depended on it, then he cupped her cheek in his palm. "And I want you to understand that it's going to mean a whole lot more to me than just a roll in the hay."

She shouldn't do this, Sunny told herself. Not only would it complicate things terribly, it would also make it so hard to leave him. On the other hand, she thought, it was impossible to think of leaving without experiencing this one night in his arms.

"Show me." Her eyes, wide with innocence and shimmering with desire, gleamed in the moonlight. "I want you to show me those wonderful things you promised me. Take me to those magical places I couldn't imagine."

Her voice was throaty, her slender body trembled. Looking down at her, Clint realized what a gift she was bestowing on him and said a small, silent prayer that he'd be worthy.

"Oh, darlin'," he said, drawing her back into his arms and holding her close, "I'm going to try my damndest."

Later, thinking back on it, Sunny had no memory of Clint turning off the car radio, of walking with him to her room, or of one of them unlocking the door.

But somehow all that must have happened because the next thing she knew she was standing beside the double bed, more nervous than she'd ever been before in her life.

"You are so beautiful."

At her request, he'd left off the cowboy boot lamp, but had opened the drapes, to allow the silver dollar moon to light the room. Although Sunny knew that no one could see in, the uncovered window created a subconscious fear of discovery that made what they were doing seem even more exciting. Forbidden.

Clint ran his palms over her shoulders with a tenderness that caused a lump in her throat and made her want to weep.

"The most beautiful woman I've ever known," he murmured.

Sunny knew he was exaggerating. But his words made her heart sprout wings, nevertheless.

"Did I mention that I love this outfit?"

The beaded ivory lace blouse with its sweetheart neckline, flowing sleeves and matching pleated skirt had magically appeared in her suitcase. Although she'd worried it would be overkill for the Boot Hill Saloon, she'd been unable to resist. From the looks she'd garnered, and not just from Clint, she'd realized that Andromeda had chosen well.

"I believe you said something about it," she murmured. "When you picked me up after the rodeo."

"It's lovely. But I think you're a bit overdressed."

With a deftness she found amazing, he slipped the tiny pearl buttons through the loops, one at a time, then kissed each bit of revealed flesh. When he got to her waist, he tugged the blouse free of the waistband, and sent it fluttering to the floor.

"Do you like that?" he murmured against her throat.

"Oh, yes," she breathed.

"I'm glad." His lips skimmed across her collarbone, creating sparks. "How about this?" He touched his mouth to the crest of her breast, and was rewarded when she gasped, then sighed.

When she didn't immediately answer, he caught her chin between his fingers, causing her to open her eyes. "You're going to have to tell me what you want, Sunny."

"I want you."

His lips quirked. "Well, sweetheart, that's definitely mutual. But you see, there are a lot of in-between things. So, I thought I'd just go step by step and you could let me know whether or not you liked what I was doing."

She couldn't imagine not liking anything he might think to do to her. "I liked that," she murmured, relieved he couldn't see her blushing. "A lot."

He laughed at that, not because she'd said anything funny, but because he felt so damn good. "Well, I'm real pleased about that. Because I liked it a lot, too." To underscore his words, he lowered his mouth to that gardenia soft flesh again and dampened it with his tongue.

"Oh, yes," she whispered. He'd promised that there was more than kissing, but she'd never expected this. Entranced by the heat of his wonderful mouth, she was suddenly shaken when he backed away. "Clint?"

"Your turn."

When she stared uncomprehendingly at him, he held out his arms, twisting his wrists so the buttons on his cuffs were turned up. "To take my shirt off."

"Oh." Much more nervous than she'd been when he'd begun to work on her buttons, Sunny started with the sleeves. "Why do you have three buttons on each sleeve?"

"For looks. The saleslady told me women love these cuffs."

"Not women trying to undress their man," she muttered as she managed to unfasten the left sleeve.

Their man. Clint couldn't remember when any woman had referred to him as her man. Even Laura's loyalties had been mixed. And although he'd understood how hard it had been for her to break her vows, there had been more than a few times when he'd been frustrated by her unwillingness, or inability, to put him first.

Not wanting to think of Laura tonight, he pushed the thoughts of her into a far distant corner of his mind. That same safe place where he'd kept her during all those years they'd been apart.

"What me to help?" he asked.

"No." Her teeth were worrying her bottom lip as she struggled to unfasten the resistant buttons.

Success! His cuffs open, Sunny moved on to the front of his shirt, her fingers moving with more confidence. She tugged the cloth free of his jeans to reach the bottom buttons, then folded the material back.

He was the most stunning man she'd ever seen. As hard and spectacular as the land where he'd chosen to live. She reached out and touched the coppery flesh with her suddenly sensitive fingertips, and discovered that the same heat that had flamed in her was burning in him.

Drawn to that hot skin, she kissed it, murmuring a soft sound of pleasure as she drank in the intimate dark taste and breathed in the earthy male scent. She felt his muscles bunch up tight as her lips skimmed over them, and marveled at the texture of the soft ebony hair against her cheek.

Clint Garvey was all she'd dreamed of as a mortal woman, the only thing on this planet she desired.

And he wasn't hers.

When that thought struck home, she felt colder than she'd felt while lying in that snowdrift.

Clint felt her suddenly stiffen, heard her soft murmurs turn into a faint moan.

"Sunny?"

He caught hold of her bare shoulders and put her a little away from him. "What's wrong?"

"Nothing." Blinking away the treacherous tears caused by that depressing thought, she gave him a watery little smile that didn't fool him for a moment.

"I want you so much right now, I can hardly breathe," he told her. "But if you don't want to do this . . ."

"No." Panicky, she pressed her fingers against his lips to block his words. "I want you to make love to me because of the way you make me feel when you kiss me. When you touch me. When you look at me the way you looked at me while we were dancing. The way you're looking at me now."

Understanding that there'd be a price to pay for breaking so many rules, but willing to risk everything for this one glorious, spellbinding night, Sunny went up on her toes and touched her mouth to his.

"I want you to make love to me more than I've ever wanted anything in my life. In fact, I think I'll go crazy if you don't."

It was all he needed to hear. "Can't have that," he said, conveniently forgetting he'd accused her of being crazy for making up that fairy godmother story. His lips curved beneath hers as he slowly backed her up toward the bed.

"I'm going to do things to you, Sunny." His smile was warm and wicked as he sat her down and knelt to pull off her boots. "Wonderful, exciting, impossible, exquisite things."

The first boot hit the floor with a barely heard thud. When he surprised her by touching his lips to her instep, Sunny imagined she heard her skin sizzle.

"Then, you're going to do amazing, dangerous, exhilarating, glorious things to me." The second boot followed. This time he kissed the small round bone on her ankle, creating a surge of heat that shot up her leg to that warm wet place between her thighs.

"And then—" he lifted her skirt and followed the sizzling heat with his mouth, barely touching her flesh, hinting at erotic things to come "—we're going to do all those magical things to each other."

His words were satin cords, twining around her heart, then his, binding them together.

Passion rose, sweet and thick as honey. Desire lapped over Sunny like the warm wavelets of a tropical ocean. As he pressed her back against the pillows, pleasure floated dreamlike over her mind.

And as his hands finished undressing Sunny, and his clever, wicked, wonderful lips treated each bit of freed flesh to a sweet sensual torment, all thought, all reason, drifted away.

He then proceeded to dispense with his own clothes with a lazy ease that suggested he was not at all shy about being naked in front of a woman.

And why should he be? Sunny wondered as she looked up at him. He was, in a word, magnificent. Whipcord lean, with muscles that rippled and gleamed in the silvery moondust streaming into the room. His thighs were strong from a lifetime spent on horseback, his arms were sinewy from controlling the twelve-hundred-pound animals.

His chest, tanned to a coppery hue by the Arizona sun, had a light sprinkling of dark hair. As her gaze followed that arrowing of hair to the fully aroused darkness between his rigid thighs, Sunny felt a hammering in her throat that she barely recognized as her own heart.

When she slowly lifted her eyes back to his face, she was embarrassed to realize he was aware of her prolonged scrutiny. She expected some masculinely smug remark, but instead, he captured her rapt attention as he trailed his splayed hand slowly down his chest, then curled his long dark fingers around his tumescent flesh.

"You do that," he told her, his voice gruff with hunger. "It's because of you." She watched in awe as he trailed a finger from the nest of jet curls to the tip. "It's all for you."

"Oh, yes." She was struck with a sudden, almost overwhelming urge to lick away the single drop of pearly moisture shimmering at the plum-hued tip. But her limbs were too heavy to move.

Clint's penis throbbed in the hand that was a lousy substitute for her touch. Needing to feel her pale, satin skin against his, he lay down beside her on the bed, combed his hands through her hair and kissed her. A long, deep, hot kiss that left them both trembling.

Forcing down the need to bury himself deep in her soft, feminine warmth, Clint reined in his raging desire, reminding himself that they had all night. And then, if he had anything to say about it, a lifetime.

His hands moved over her, with a lazy, intimate touch that made her feel as if she were adrift on a soft sea of desire, willing to go wherever destiny, and Clint, took her.

She'd known he was a good man. But she never could have imagined how much control Clint had. Even as her flesh heated and her breathing quickened, even as she began to writhe restlessly on the cotton sheets, he insisted on tenderly taking his time.

He rained kisses up the bones of her spine, creating a sizzling heat against her moist flesh. He laved her aching breasts, then took the ultrasensitive nipples into his mouth, each in turn, tugging on them in a way that created a rush of wet heat between her legs, which he lapped up in a way that shocked and thrilled her. And had her quaking with elemental need.

"Like rose petals," he murmured against her, his voice sending thrumming waves of sound and heat spiraling outward. "All pink and soft and damp with morning dew."

When that devastating tongue touched the tingling hard bud that was practically screaming for his touch, Sunny sighed in pleased wonder as she crested in a gentle wave that lifted up, then settled.

Steadfastly ignoring the needs of his own aching body, Clint held her close as the faint tremors slowly abated.

"That was wonderful," she murmured, snuggling up against him. "I never imagined anything could feel so lovely."

"Oh, we're not finished, sunshine," he promised. "Not hardly."

When he left the bed, Sunny felt instantly bereft. She reached out for him. "Clint . . ."

"Just one little minute, darlin'," he promised as he took the foil package from the pocket of the discarded jeans. She watched, intrigued as he tore the package open with his teeth, then rolled the condom over his erection.

Watching her practically eating him up with those wide, avid eyes, made Clint feel more powerful than he'd ever felt. In fact, right now, he felt downright invincible.

"Watch carefully," he said with a slow, seductive smile. "Because next time you get to do this."

The sensuous idea caused a slow burn that went all the way to Sunny's bones.

Wanting to watch her this time, he kept his gaze on her face as his hand moved downward between their bodies and intimately cupped the still pulsing flesh, causing her to flinch.

"Don't worry." He kissed her reassuringly. "I'd never hurt you. You have to trust me."

"I do." Her affirmation was echoed in her passion-laced eyes.

"That's the girl." He slipped one finger into her, felt her tense, then relax. "I love you like this," he murmured, his eyes still on hers. He slipped in a second finger. "All warm. And willing." As he began to take them out again, Clint felt her body clutch at him. "And wonderful."

As he moved his fingers in and out of her with a wet, silky ease, Sunny learned what it was to ache for someone. Learned what it was to feel so much, and still need more. Discovered that passion went beyond all imagined possibilities.

Her body tensed. Her skin felt unbearably sensitized as he took her on a thrilling ride, higher and higher to where the air was thin and stole her breath, down again to where it was thick and laden with passion, and then, impossibly, drove her to even greater heights until Sunny felt suspended on a steep, rocky precipice of desire.

Needs vibrated through her, vivid, spinning colors swirled behind her eyes, as his wicked, wondrous tongue raked her clitoris, causing her cry out his name on a strangled sob as she went plummeting over the edge.

Clint held back, wanting to give Sunny everything he had to give, and decided that watching her eyes widen, then cloud, seeing the rosy flush, like a fever, suffusing her flesh was the sexiest thing he'd ever seen.

Sunny gazed up at Clint, saw the pleasure her response had given him and understood that her surrender had been a gift. A gift that had empowered her, allowing her to take. And, in turn, to give. She wrapped her arms around him and pressed her open mouth against the pulsing blood beat at the base of his throat.

"I love you," she whispered against his damp dark skin.

Those three little words, spoken so softly, were all that it took to cause his hard-fought control to snap.

Although he'd tried to be patient, had fought to remain tender, the animal had taken over: the need to possess her ripped at him with sharp, vicious claws.

"You're mine, Sunny." Using his superior weight to press her deep into the too soft mattress, he moved against her, his muscles taut and gleaming with passion.

Gazing up at him, she viewed the menacing man she'd first seen holding that deadly gun. How could she have forgotten this dark side of him? How could she not have known that danger could be so erotic? So thrilling.

Her words caught in her throat; she could only nod.

It wasn't enough. Just as he'd needed to watch her go over the edge, Clint needed to hear the words out loud.

"Say it," he insisted, rubbing against her in a way that aroused more than intimidated.

"I'm yours," she managed.

He lifted her hips, his fingers digging painfully into her flesh. "Forever."

His eyes were aflame, his touch was going to leave bruises and his mouth was set in that grim line she hadn't seen for days. What he was asking was impossible. But Sunny had neither the strength nor the will to tell him that sad truth now.

"Forever." The lie came out on a choked sob. Then, digging her fingers into his upper arms, she lifted her hips even higher off the tangled sheets and opened for him, body, mind and heart.

Clint surged into her tight wet sheath with a single thrust, burying himself deep in her warmth. As he began to move, hard and fast, he could have sworn he smelled wildflowers.

Then he took them both racing into the swirling, smoky darkness, where passion ruled and time had no meaning. As he gave Sunny everything he'd promised, as he took everything he so desperately needed, there was no yesterday. No tomorrow.

There was only this suspended moment.

He felt her convulse around him, and only then did he finally give in to his own release.

THE EARLY MORNING sun was streaming through the window, creating dancing diamonds on the Navajo white walls. Suspended between sleep and wakefulness, Sunny considered getting up to close the drapes but decided she was too comfortable, too happy, right where she was.

The garish striped bedspread and blanket had landed on the floor sometime during the night and the only thing covering her body was a tangle of well-worn sheet. And Clint's arms and legs, wrapped around her, holding her close, warming her like a thick downy quilt. Her hand lay over his heart. She could feel its steady rhythm, so different from its earlier wild pounding beneath her palm.

She let her eyes drift shut again, burrowed into his comforting embrace and allowed her mind to wander.

Last night had been the most incredible night of her life. She'd lost track of how many times she and Clint had made love, but the last time had been well into the morning, only a few hours ago. She knew she should be exhausted, but in truth, she'd never felt more alive in her life.

She'd never realized lovemaking could be like that. She hadn't believed that mortals could experience magic. But Clint had proven her wrong. What they'd shared had been exhilarating, glorious and absolutely magical.

Sunny almost laughed, but knowing Clint was going to have to climb back onto a wild bucking animal in a few hours, she didn't want to wake him. So she merely smiled, molded herself to the warm hard wall of his bare chest and recalled in vivid detail how his roughened hands had felt like the finest grade of sandpaper as they'd moved over her body, stimulating her nerve endings until they'd crackled like heat lightning on the horizon before a mountain thunderstorm.

And his mouth—so wicked, so hot, so greedy! It made her body yearn all over again just thinking back on all the impossible pleasures it had brought her.

But there'd been a great deal more than mere sex involved in what had happened last night. The words she had spoken, the promise she had made would have to be dealt with.

Her mood, which only a moment ago had been so happy, swung downward like a pendulum. Sunny pressed her lips against Clint's chest, squeezing back the tears that threatened as she thought about the day ahead. It wouldn't be easy, doing what she had to do. But she'd do it, Sunny vowed. For Clint. Because she loved him.

As her mind struggled with feelings too complex to catalogue, and thoughts too depressing to think about, she closed her eyes tight and drifted back into a soft-edged sleep and dreamed of what might have been.

13

CLINT WATCHED SUNNY sleep, and wondered what he'd ever done in his life to deserve this miraculous second chance at love. And, although he knew it went against every vestige of the common sense he'd always prided himself on, he'd somehow fallen in love with this woman who'd literally burst into his life less than a week ago.

He didn't know who she was. Didn't know anything about her, really, except she cooked like Julia Child, tasted like the sweetest bit of heaven and had a smile as bright and benevolent as a summer sun. She'd assured him that she wasn't running away from a husband, and Clint had no choice but to believe her.

But it wouldn't have mattered if she was married. Because in every way, she belonged to him. She'd come out of nowhere, and had ambushed him at the darkest moment in his life. She'd stolen his heart while turning his world upside down, then had put it back into place, amazingly restored again, last night.

And in return, he'd branded her as his own. Sunny was his, Clint vowed. Forever.

Outside, across the street, the rodeo was coming to life. Inside, he could hear the sound of the shower in the room next door, the drone of the television, the murmur of voices. The day was beginning, whether he wanted it to or not.

Clint found himself more than a little tempted to forgo
the final day's events and just stay right here in bed with
Sunny.

As if aware of his intense scrutiny, she slowly roused,
blinking as she stared up at him with sleep-heavy eyes.

"Hi," she whispered. A new day had dawned, forcing
her to face the inevitable.

"Hi yourself." Something was wrong. Clint sensed it;
saw it in the tense set of her shoulders, the hesitancy in her
eyes.

Believing she was suffering from an understandable case
of morning-after self-consciousness, he refrained from
kissing her, as he'd been longing to do, and ran the back
of his hand down the side of her face instead.

"How are you feeling?"

"Fine," she answered promptly. The sheet had drifted
down to her waist. Uncomfortable carrying on this conversation in broad daylight while wearing nothing at all,
she pulled the sheet up to her chin.

He almost laughed at her futile attempt at modesty. As
if he didn't have the memory of every ounce of that fra-
grant flesh imbedded in his mind. "The truth, Sunny." He
trailed his fingers around her chin, down her throat. "How
are you really feeling?"

The tender touch, meant to soothe, only succeeded in
making her more nervous. "Fine," she insisted, her frail
voice telling him otherwise.

He tugged the sheet back down, then ran a fingertip over
the crests of her breasts, and frowned at the faint black-
and-blue bruises marring the porcelain flesh.

"I hurt you."

"You could never hurt me." But she would hurt him,
Sunny feared, reminding herself that although he might

not believe it now, the end really would justify the means. No matter how unpleasant they may be.

"Never on purpose," he promised, unwittingly making her feel even more guilty.

Unable to look at him, Sunny dragged her gaze out the window. "It's almost time for the first event."

"Mmm." Drawn by her scent, he nuzzled her neck. "Lucky for us I'm not in the first event." His lips were hypnotic, seducing her into compliance. Sunny felt that now familiar drugging haze drifting over her mind. "I was watching you sleep," he said.

So she'd been right. She had felt him. Sunny was not encouraged by the fact that they'd established a mental link.

"Want to know what I was thinking?"

"That I snore?" she asked, and managed a small smile.

"Cute, sunshine." Because it had been too long since he'd kissed her, he touched his lips to hers.

Her mouth seemed to have taken on a mind of its own, and clung of its own volition to his. Sunny was both relieved and disappointed when he finally broke off the sweet lingering kiss.

"I was thinking how much I'd like to spend the day here in bed with you. But then I realized you'd probably be a little sore this morning, so I figured I might as well do some rodeoing, then come back here and let you drive me crazy again all night." He ruffled her tousled hair and smiled down at her. "Then, I thought I'd call Mariah, who'll be glad to take care of things for a few more days, and we could play tourist."

He'd picked up her hand and was idly kissing each fingertip as he talked. "You can't come to Tombstone without seeing the O.K. Corral, then I thought maybe we'd drive to Tucson or Phoenix, and use some of my winnings to book a room in one of the resorts—maybe we'll even spring for a suite, with a Jacuzzi, and—"

"Clint." She pressed her free hand against his unshaven cheek. "I can't."

He stiffened, almost imperceptibly. But Sunny, who was watching him intently, did not miss the tightening of his magnificent body, or the muscle that had suddenly clenched beneath her fingertips. "Can't what?"

His voice was calm and measured; his eyes were not.

"I can't play tourist with you."

"Sure you can. If you're worried about your boss giving you a few days off, Sunny, don't worry." He flashed her a playful, lecherous grin that didn't reach his ice blue eyes. "I hear the guy's a sucker for a certain pretty woman. If you just play your cards right—"

"I can't play tourist with you." She pulled away from his tender touch.

"If you'd rather go straight back to Whiskey River—"

"I can't do that, either."

Cold anger whipped through him. "Want to tell me why not?"

Even knowing how difficult it was going to be to leave him, Sunny had not been prepared for the pain of his anger.

"I've already told you," she managed to whisper, the words almost strangling her as her nervous hands unconsciously gathered up the edge of the sheet. "I'm not the right woman for you."

"Bull!" He wanted to take hold of her shoulders and shake her. "Don't you think I know when a woman's right for me? When I'm right for a woman?"

He leaned forward until their foreheads were almost touching. His eyes blazed into hers, his breath was a hot wind on her face. "You may be a good actress, sweetheart, but you sure as hell aren't good enough to fake those orgasms I gave you. If you'd shaken any harder, this place would have come down around us. And if you'd screamed any louder, someone would have called the cops."

The accusations were like bullets that struck directly in her heart. Sunny couldn't believe real bullets could have been any more painful.

"I wasn't acting." Her breathing was ragged, her voice trembled. "I could never have lied about that." She swallowed a violent tremor. "But there's more to a relationship than sex."

Clint stared down at her in disbelief. For a moment, it seemed his body had shut down: his mind, his heart, his lungs. On some distant level he told himself he should be grateful. It was difficult to feel the pain when you were numb.

"And that's all last night meant to you?" he asked in a cool, remote voice that sent a shiver down her spine. For some reason the icy anger frightened her more than the earlier hot fury.

She nodded, unable to speak past the lump in her throat. Unable to breathe for the iron fist twisting her chest.

He continued to stare at her for a long, silent time. Wanting to tell him all that last night had meant to her, wanting to assure him that she'd never, ever forget the magical time they'd shared, desperate to cry out that she loved him and always would until the end of time, Sunny bit her lip and turned away.

"Damn you." The muttered curse was followed by a riper, harsher one. She heard him gathering up his clothes, was vaguely aware of him pulling them on. And then he was gone, slamming the door behind him.

Sunny watched as the painting of Wyatt Earp facing down the Clanton brothers tilted. Another, depicting

Geronimo astride a horrendously ill-proportioned horse fell off the wall, and landed on the ugly orange carpet with a muffled thud.

The lingering silence was suffocating. And crushing. Lowering her face to her hands, Sunny finally allowed herself to weep.

Dora found her like that, curled up on the bed, unable to think, unable to feel.

"Sorry to come right in," the older woman said cautiously, "but when you didn't answer your door, I thought you maybe fell in the shower, or . . ." Her voice drifted off. "Aw hell, who am I kidding? I was worried about you and came to see if you were all right."

"I'm fine," Sunny mumbled into the pillow she was holding. The pillow that still carried Clint's scent. "Why were you worried?"

"Because Clint looks like Desperado spent the night stomping on his heart."

"It wasn't the night." Sunny sighed and closed her eyes, reliving the glorious images in her mind. "The night was wonderful."

"I see." Without waiting for an invitation, Dora sat down on the bed and ran her hand down Sunny's hair in a maternal gesture so warm and tender Sunny almost started crying again. "Sometimes those morning-afters can be a little awkward."

"This was more than awkward."

"Yeah, I kinda got that impression looking at Clint. You know, hon, although I do hate to sound like Rooster, breaking in a man is a lot like breaking in a horse. You gotta take it slow and easy. And not rush him."

Although some of Rooster's cowboyisms had gone over Sunny's head, she understood this one. "It wasn't that way.

Actually, it's my fault. Clint wanted more than I could give."

"Oh." Although Dora sounded surprised that any woman wouldn't be eager to scoop up a great catch like Clint Garvey, Sunny was grateful to her for keeping her thoughts to herself. "Well, you know what the Duke's wife always said."

"What's that?"

"A gal's gotta do what a gal's gotta do." When that earned a reluctant smile, Dora grinned. "That's better. And by the way, I'm not gettin' into your business, but Clint asked me to give you a message."

"Oh?"

"Noel Giraudeau had her baby."

"She did?" That got Sunny's attention. What mortal woman could ignore such happy news? "What was it?"

"A little girl. Mariah told Clint that they named her Marisa."

"Marisa Giraudeau," Sunny murmured. "That's a lovely name."

"Sure is." Dora nodded. "But the one they gave her is even better. Marisa Reardon."

"Reardon?"

"Noel and Mac got married in the hospital," Dora revealed with a grin. "Between contractions. Mariah, Tara and Jessica Ingersoll—Clint said you haven't met her yet—stood up with her.

"The way Mariah tells it, right after Noel promised to love, honor and cherish, she swore to kill Mac if he ever came near her again."

Dora's laugh was bold and rich, encouraging an answering one from Sunny. "They're so lucky," she murmured.

"True enough," the older woman agreed. "But sometimes we can make our own luck. Not that I'm messing in your business," she said again.

That was far from the truth, Sunny knew, nevertheless she was grateful to have another woman to share her unhappiness with.

"You missed the Jaycee's pancake breakfast," Dora said.

Sunny sighed. "I wasn't hungry."

"I can understand that. But a girl's gotta eat. Rooster and I figured we'd take you out to breakfast at the O.K. Corral Café before we head over to the fairgrounds."

"Oh, I can't . . ."

Sunny was about to insist that she couldn't go to the rodeo, but stopped. Since there was no future for her and Clint, it was better to make a clean break. But even as her head tried to look at the situation rationally, her heart knew that she couldn't leave without ensuring that Clint had survived the dangerous competition.

"It'll take me fifteen minutes to get ready," she said.

Dora's satisfied smile suggested she'd never expected any other answer. "Take your time. There's still another hour before Clint's got to ride Lightning Jack."

"Lightning Jack?" Sunny had studied the program carefully yesterday, and knew that the horse was nearly as bad as Desperado. "What bull did he draw?" she asked.

Dora's eyes shifted away, pretending intense interest in the painting lying on the carpet across the room. "Isn't that something?" she mused. "I wonder what Geronimo's doin' wearing a Sioux chief's feather headdress?"

"Creative license," Sunny guessed. "Dora?" Her tone had regained its strength. "What bull did Clint draw?"

Dora heaved a heavy sigh. "Terminator."

The same bull that had gored that young cowboy yesterday. This bull didn't just want to throw any cowboy

who had the audacity to try to ride him, he wanted to kill
him.

Sunny's heart sank.

SUNNY, DORA AND Rooster arrived at the arena just in
time to watch Charmayne spur Buttermilk around the
barrels to a blazing fifteen-second time that easily captured first place. Dressed in a sparkly red-white-and-blue
shirt, her black hair flying out from beneath the snowy
white Stetson as she charged toward the finish line, Charmayne looked like nothing less than a champion.

As was Clint. Once again Sunny reminded herself that
she'd chosen well. That thought, which should have given
her some small satisfaction, only made her feel even more
miserable.

Lightning Jack lived up to his name, twisting and turning and bucking so hard that even knowing how good
Clint was, Sunny was amazed he was able to stay on the
bronc's back. Today he managed to bail on his own,
without the help of the pickup rider.

"One down, one to go," Rooster said with obvious pride
as Clint's first place win was announced to thunderous
applause.

That he was popular with the crowd was obvious. That
he was even more popular with Charmayne was also obvious. The winning cowgirl planted a victory kiss on his
mouth in front of the spectators, earning an appreciative
roar from the stands, and loud hoots from the cowboys on
the sidelines.

"He definitely earned that four thousand dollars," Dora
agreed.

As depressed as she was, Sunny felt some small pleasure in having used her wish to get Clint to come to Tombstone. Even if he didn't win the bull-riding competition,

with his winnings plus the money in the barbecue jar, he was going to go home nine thousand dollars richer.

Sunny watched the calf roping, steer wrestling and bareback riding in a worried haze and was only vaguely aware of the action. All her thoughts, and her fears, were focused on Clint's upcoming bull-riding event.

And then it was time. Giant condors were flapping their huge wings in Sunny's stomach as she watched the first three riders. The bruised and battered Rope did better today, lasting six seconds on a mean-tempered bull named Jalepeño, before being thrown off. As he limped the long walk back to the chute, Sunny saw Clint waiting for the young cowboy.

He slapped Rope on the shoulder, and the two men exchanged a few words, although Clint seemed to be doing most of the talking.

"The boy could do a whole lot worse than have Clint teach him," Rooster said.

"He already showed improvement," Dora agreed.

"That wouldn't be difficult," Rooster drawled. "Considerin' he didn't make it out of the chute yesterday."

The cowboy that followed Rope was thrown as well. The clowns distracted the animal long enough for the hapless cowboy to make his way to safety, but Sunny covered her face with her hands as the bull charged toward the barrel the clown had dived into.

It was Clint's turn. Sunny's fingernails dug deep crescents into her palms as she watched Terminator ramming his horns against the gate of the chute before Clint had even climbed on his back.

And then he was on. The cowboys on the arena side of the gate scrambled as the door opened and the white-faced bull burst from the chute like an explosion of TNT, and began bucking, spinning and whirling so fast bull and rider were almost a blur.

"Hot damn!" Rooster shouted, jumping to his feet. All around Sunny spectators were doing the same. Frustrated by her inability to see, she climbed up on the bleachers in front of her and stared in disbelief.

Clint was lying almost flat on the back of the furiously bucking two-thousand-pound bovine, his left arm in the air, spurs forward, just as he had yesterday.

He lost his hat. Sunny watched as it went sailing into the dust. But still he refused to surrender to Terminator, holding on as only a champion could.

And then everything seemed to happen at once. The buzzer rang, signaling a successful ride, the crowd roared, and Clint went flying. He hit the ground, hard. Sunny cried out, although she knew hard landings were par for the course in the rodeo business.

What she saw next sent her heart into her throat.

Terminator had lowered his enormous head and was charging straight at Clint.

One of the clowns, who'd picked up Clint's hat, threw it in front of the bull to distract him. Without missing a beat, Terminator tossed the hat out of his way with a vicious horn. Another clown ran toward the animal holding out a stuffed dummy, but the bull was undeterred. When Clint, who was lying on the ground looking dazed, saw the bull headed his way, he tried to push himself up, but it was too late.

"No!" Sunny's scream rang out over the distressed cries of the crowd as Terminator zeroed in on Clint's back.

At the last moment, for no apparent reason, Terminator turned and gored the straw-stuffed cowboy instead, with such force it was ripped off the cable. Clint half ran, half crawled back to the chute where Rope and other waiting cowboys pulled him out of harm's way.

"Lordie!" Dora pressed a hand against her heart. "I think I died about a thousand deaths."

"You're not the only one," Rooster said. "Good thing my hair's already gray because it sure as hell would've gone white after that."

Dora watched as Clint was led to the waiting ambulance. "Guess we'd better get over to the hospital." She glanced over at Sunny, whose heart had still not returned to anything resembling a normal beat. "You coming?"

She shouldn't. But, loving Clint as she did, Sunny couldn't stay away. "Of course," she said simply.

14

CLINT WAS LYING in bed, his arm in a cast and sling, looking unnaturally ashen when Sunny knocked tentatively and peeked around the door.

"Am I allowed in?"

For a fleeting instant, as he looked over at her, Clint's eyes were dark and unguarded. Then, as she watched, he pulled the familiar shades down. "I can't imagine keeping you out."

His expression, and his voice were anything but encouraging, but Sunny had never been fainthearted. "You certainly gave us all a scare."

He continued to stare at her and said nothing.

"I've never seen anything that was so terrifying and thrilling at the same time. Why, even Rooster, who's definitely ridden in his share of rodeos, said—"

"What are you doing here, Sunny?"

He was very still. Impossibly still. How could he possibly remain so calm after the way they'd parted this morning? She felt as if someone had put a live wire beneath her skin.

She started to speak but the words wouldn't come. Clearing her throat, she tried again. "I was worried about you."

"I see." His eyes still on hers, he clenched his good hand into a fist on top of the sheet. "So, I guess all I have to do is break my head whenever I want your attention?"

Since the doctor had already assured her it was a mild concussion, Sunny was able to concentrate on his resentment rather than the worry she'd suffered during the short drive to the hospital in Rooster's truck.

"I suppose I deserved that."

When he didn't answer, she decided on this, at least, they were in full agreement.

"I'm sorry about your arm."

He shrugged, then wished he hadn't. "It won't be the first one I've broken." He flexed his hand, then fisted it again. "It won't be the last."

"I suppose not if you keep rodeoing."

"Actually, I decided this might be a good time to go into retirement."

Relief flooded over her. "I'd glad. Not that you're not wonderful, of course. By the way, did you know that you'd won the bull riding?"

"Yeah. The emergency room clerk took the phone call."

"Congratulations. You must be very proud, and of course the money should help cover ranch expenses until—"

"You lied, didn't you?"

"About what?" Did he know that she'd been lying when she'd suggested that last night had only been about sex? Did he suspect how deeply she loved him?

Watching the guilt move across her lovely face, Clint wanted to hit something. On the ride over in the ambulance, and later, as he'd been examined and treated in the ER, he'd run every second of the Terminator ride through his mind and realized that although Sunny may not have been entirely open about everything, there was no longer any question about who she was. Or, more important, what she was.

"About losing your powers."

"Oh, that." She managed a smile when she realized he'd finally accepted that she was, indeed, his fairy godmother. "No, I wasn't lying about that."

"Then how..." He watched her bite her bottom lip, and was struck with a powerful urge to soothe the worried flesh with his tongue. Furious at the power she had over him, Clint forced his mind back to what he needed to know.

"I rode my first bull when I was twelve. I know the damn animals, Sunny. As well as anyone can know them. I saw his eyes. He had killing on his mind. And nothing was going to stop him. Not me, not those clowns, not a damn thing . . . except magic."

"Except magic," she agreed in a whisper.

He shook his head, ignoring the concussion-caused lightning bolts behind his eyes. "I don't suppose you'd care to explain how you pulled that off, without your powers."

"I had three wishes."

"Someone who should know about such things once told me that genies were the ones with three wishes."

"Well, that's true. But Andromeda felt guilty because I'd lost my powers when I wished I was mortal—"

"Who's Andromeda?"

"Oh. My superior. She's in charge of Fairy Godmother Central's romance branch."

"I see." He didn't. Not exactly, but decided that part didn't matter.

Clint told himself that any sane man would consider this conversation merely a result of having his head cracked by falling off a bucking Brahman bull. But as impossible as it sounded, he knew otherwise.

"Anyway, she gave me three wishes, just in case. The first one I used to get you to agree to come here."

So that's what had happened. "I've been wondering about that," he admitted.

"I know it wasn't exactly a nice thing to do, playing with your mind like that. But you were being horribly stubborn—"

"That's all right. At least your heart was in the right place. And I did make some money. Of course, I also broke my arm," he added as an afterthought.

"I'm so sorry about that."

"Hell, you didn't do it." He gave her a quick hard look. "You didn't, did you?"

"Of course not!"

"And then you used your second wish to get Terminator to swerve at the last minute."

"I couldn't let you die."

"No. That's why you came to Whiskey River in the first place, isn't it?" he murmured as comprehension finally sank in. "Your assignment was to keep me from killing myself."

Sunny moistened her too dry lips. "That was how it started, yes, because I was trying to win a promotion, and you were the most difficult case Andromeda and the council could find, but—"

"But?" The blood was pounding in his head. Even knowing he'd been nothing but an assignment to her, he couldn't help wanting her.

She was twisting her hands in front of her. "But things got out of hand."

"Are you telling me you don't always sleep with your suicidal assignments?"

His cool voice was like a thousand needles of ice stabbing into her heart. "You know better than that."

The hurt in her eyes filled him with self-disgust. Of course he knew better. Wasn't he the one who'd taken her innocence? Which wasn't a bad trade-off, he decided. Since somehow, when he hadn't been looking, she'd stolen his heart.

Clint knew he should apologize, but his wounded pride wouldn't let him.

"So," he said with a casualness he was a very long way from feeling, "what are you going to do with the third wish?"

Sunny couldn't speak; could barely think. She let out a long breath and prayed for composure. Pride would not let her crumble to pieces in front of him.

"I'm going to use it to go home," she said finally.

He should have seen it coming. He wanted to get up, lock the door, drag her down onto his bed, by the hair, if necessary, and let her know that he wasn't going to let her go anywhere. Because, dammit, she was his. She'd sworn she was and he damn well intended to hold her to her promise.

That was what he wanted to do. But couldn't.

"Of course," he murmured, his voice tighter and colder than she'd ever heard it. "I should have thought of that."

Sunny couldn't bear the thought of Clint going through life hating her when all she wanted, all she'd ever wanted, was for him to be happy.

"Clint—" She started toward the bed, needing to touch him, to hold him.

"Are you staying?"

Tears filled her eyes, her throat. "I can't," she whispered, shaking her head.

"Then go." He turned his head and looked out the window at the parking lot. "It was fun while it lasted, Sunny. Enjoy your promotion. You've been a crackerjack fairy godmother. If you ever need a reference, have dear old Andromeda get in touch with me."

The animosity filled the room like a dark, dank cloud. Unable to think of any way to salvage the mess she'd made, Sunny turned and fled before she made things even worse.

She was on her way out of the hospital when she saw the unmistakable pink pickup drive up. Sunny stopped and looked up at the window of Clint's room.

There was, she realized, one more thing she could do.

"Please," she wished, watching as Charmayne got out of the truck and began walking toward the double doors of the hospital, "please make things work out for Clint. Make him live the rest of his life with his perfect love match."

This time, her wish did not go unanswered. "Are you sure this is what you want, Sunny?" Andromeda's calm voice echoed in Sunny's mind. "Even knowing that if we agree to grant this wish, you'll be forced to stay on earth and live as a mortal woman?"

Sunny watched the automatic doors open, watched Charmayne breeze through them with an air of self-confidence that suggested the spell had already taken effect. She looked up at the window again and wondered if Clint was looking back at her.

All she'd ever wanted was for him to be happy. And now, Sunny thought with a little hitch in her heart, he would be.

"Yes." She whispered the answer. Then said it again, louder. "Yes."

Her assignment completed, she allowed Dora and Rooster to take her back to the motel. She had packing to do. And a life to begin.

"JUST A MINUTE!" Sunny called out in answer to the knock at the motel room door. She opened the door expecting to find Dora, come to give her a ride to the bus station. Instead, she was stunned to find herself standing face-to-face with Clint.

"What are you doing here?"

"Is that any way to welcome the Tombstone Jamboree's reigning bull-riding champion?" he asked, entering the room uninvited.

"Why aren't you in the hospital?"

"I checked myself out."

"But your arm—"

"Is only broken." He ran his free hand over her shoulder. "Damn, you're tense, sweetheart. Maybe we ought to try to loosen you up."

She moved back one step. "You've had a concussion."

Clint took two steps toward her. "Only a minor one. I've had worse." They continued their little back and forth dance around the cramped room. "If you keep running away from me, sunshine, I'm going to have to get my rope out of the truck and lasso you."

"You don't belong here." He'd managed to maneuver her between the bed and the wall, effectively cutting off her escape.

"Of course I do." He smoothed her hair, as if to reassure her, but mostly to please himself. "The question, my lovely, seductive fairy godmother is, what are you still doing here?"

"I was packing."

He glanced over at the suitcase, open on the bed. "I see. You know, I'd never call you a liar, sweetheart, but I find it a bit difficult to believe that rodeo gear is the latest fashion craze at Fairy Godmother Central."

Having lied enough for a lifetime—several lifetimes— Sunny decided to tell the truth now. "No. It's not."

"I didn't think so." He tilted forward, his eyes not leaving hers as he brushed his lips against her mouth. "You used up your last wish, didn't you?"

His clever lips were plucking at hers, coaxing her into submission. Sunny lifted her hands to his shoulders but could not muster up the strength to push him away.

"Didn't you?" His mouth was warm and certain. Hers, which had been warm but unyielding, slowly softened as she surrendered to the pleasure of the kiss. To him.

"Yes."

"I knew it." He moved forward, literally backing Sunny up against the wall, which allowed him to press his body against hers.

"I wished for you to be happy."

"Yet another wish come true," he murmured, skimming his lips up her face. He'd come here to seduce her, but as always, as he drank in her wildflower scent and tasted the sweet satin of her skin, Clint found himself becoming seduced.

She tilted her head, giving him access to her neck, and was thrilled when he complied. "With Charmayne."

"Charmayne?" He stared down at her. "Charmayne Hunter?" When she nodded, he laughed. "And I thought that Hatfield and McCoy mismatch was a doozie." He shook his head, his smile wider than she'd ever seen it.

Pride surfaced. "I'm so pleased you're amused."

"Hell, yes, I am," Clint said. "All this time you've been trying to tell me that you were the wrong woman for me. If you'd only told me who you considered the right woman, I'd have told you that I'd rather spend my life with a nest of rattlers than Charmayne Hunter."

"You're a perfect match," she insisted, wondering what had happened to her wish. "You both grew up on ranches—"

"So did hundreds of other women, including Kitty Campbell and Dora. But I don't see you trying to fix me up with them."

Sunny refused to acknowledge that ridiculous statement. "You both ride in the rodeo."

"Now there's a reason to get married," he agreed.

"She's gorgeous and you're—"

Sunny immediately shut her mouth. She was growing irritated by his continued refusal to acknowledge that this time she'd managed the perfect love match, and saw no point in boosting his ego any higher.

"I'm what?" Irresistible devils danced in his eyes.

"You're not a bad looking man," she admitted a bit grumpily.

"Why, thank you, Sunny. With flowery compliments like that, I'm sure not going to outgrow my hat anytime soon."

"She's the right one," Sunny insisted weakly.

"What did you wish, exactly?" He lowered his head again and began nibbling at her earlobe in a way that made her toes curl in her cowgirl boots.

"Wish?"

He was a wizard, she decided. That was the only explanation for the way he could continually cloud her mind.

"The third wish. What did you say?"

When he switched to the other ear, Sunny sighed. "I wished that you could live out the rest of your life with the woman who was the perfect match for you."

"Bingo." His mouth returned to hers and she could feel his satisfied smile against her lips. "That's you, sunshine."

"I can't be."

"Yes. You can." He deepened the kiss for a long glorious time and she began to think he just might be right. "You're a gorgeous, sweet-smelling, good-hearted woman, but you're a disaster just waiting to happen as a fairy godmother. I figure the least I can do for all those unsuspecting, unattached people out there is to get you out of the business."

He put his wide dark hand against her cheek and held her still hesitant gaze to his. "I didn't realize I'd wished for you, Sunny, but I sure as hell must have, because here you are and I love you to distraction, and the only thing I want for Christmas—for all the Christmases to come—is for you to come back to Whiskey River and be my wife."

She felt the very human tears overflowing her eyes, but her smile assured him that they were tears of joy. She linked her fingers around his neck, because her heart suddenly felt so light, she feared if she didn't hold on to him, she'd go floating up to the ceiling.

"Oh, yes." As she lifted her head for his kiss, Sunny realized that as long as she and Clint had each other, they'd always have magic.

Epilogue

One year later

IT WAS SNOWING. Puffy white flakes floated down from the sky like goose down. As Clint rode back to the house, thoughts of Sunny waiting for him kept him warm.

He'd been to Laura's grave, just as he had last Christmas. And, as he probably would every Christmas yet to come. It wasn't that he hadn't gotten over her, because he had. And it wasn't because he was still grieving for his lost child, because the baby that tragically hadn't lived to be born already had a home in his heart.

Clint realized how lucky he was that Sunny didn't mind the visits on the anniversary of Laura's death and again during the holidays. She understood, better than most people, that there were many types of love. And confident in his love for her, she wasn't threatened by the bittersweet feelings he continued to have for the first girl he'd ever loved.

Laura may have been his first love, but Sunny was definitely his last. Clint could barely remember what his life had been like before she'd burst into it; didn't want to imagine a world without her in it.

She was, without a doubt, the best thing that had ever happened to him. And not a day went by that he didn't thank God, or Andromeda, or whoever it was who'd sent her to her.

She'd even managed to help save his ranch with her city slickers' scheme. Last year's profit had pulled them out of debt and they were already booked to capacity for next year's spring roundup.

He stabled his mare, rubbed her down and gave her some fresh feed and water. Then he walked back to the house and into the kitchen, where he inhaled the scent of pumpkin pies baking.

"Noel phoned," Sunny called from the living room when she heard the door open. "She and Mac are going to be a little bit late. They have to drop by the drugstore and pick up some teething gel for Marisa.

"Jess and Rory are on their way, but they still have to stop and pick up Tara and Gavin. Oh, and Trace called from Flagstaff and said Mariah's plane is late getting in from L.A., but they should be here within the next couple of hours. And Dora and Rooster are still in Payson, checking out the new cutting horse you're thinking of buying."

He found her standing on a ladder, hanging yet another ornament on the tree they'd spent all last weekend decorating. The job would have gone faster if they'd kept their mind on their work, he admitted, smiling at the memory of how lovely her skin had looked, bathed in the sparkling white fairy lights.

"So, if everyone's been delayed, it sounds as if we've got about an hour to kill. Any suggestions about how we can spend it?"

Her smile warmed as she stepped down from the ladder and into his outstretched arms. "I think such two perfectly matched individuals should be able to figure out something. If we put our minds to it."

He began to unbutton her blouse. "Honey, your mind, as brilliant as it may be, is definitely not what I'm interested in right now."

Later, as Clint pulled on his jeans, he wondered how it was that every time he made love to his wife it was like the first time. If it wasn't for their anniversary dinner party tonight, he'd find it hard to believe they'd actually been married a year.

"Where did this come from?" he asked as he noticed the snow globe that hadn't been on top of the dresser when he'd dressed that morning. Inside the glass sphere was a porcelain figure of an infant in a cradle.

Sunny'd come out of the shower, wrapped in a towel that Clint was tempted, even after all they'd just shared, to pull away. "Three guesses. It was there when I came upstairs to make the bed this morning." Her smile widened. "I think it's Andromeda's way of telling me she's pleased about my news."

There was something in her voice. Something lushly feminine that, now that he studied her more closely, Clint realized was echoed in her gleaming gold eyes.

"Are you saying . . . You're not . . ."

"You're going to be a father, Clint."

"A baby?" He stared at her, trying to remember if he'd noticed any difference in her body when they'd been making love earlier. "When?"

"According to Dr. McGraw, you should begin losing sleep around the second week in August." Her smile was as warm as any a mortal woman had ever shared with her man.

"A baby." He shook his head, trying to absorb the news. He'd been so happy with Sunny, he hadn't given any thought to children. Now he realized he'd been afraid to press his luck, to wish for too much.

He pulled her into his arms and held her tightly, wishing he didn't ever have to let her go, terrified something might happen to her before—

"Clint." Her gentle voice interrupted his whirling thoughts. When she framed his face between her palms, the gold band on her left hand gleamed in the lamplight. "It's going to be all right. I'm going to be all right. And we're going to have a wonderful family."

"Yes." Fear left on a rush of pent-up breath, and was replaced with awe.

"A family," he murmured, touching his lips to hers. As the wonder of that idea filled his mind and his heart, Clint laughed. "And they all lived happily ever after."

Spoil yourself next month
with these four novels from

OUTRAGEOUS by Lori Foster

Blaze—red-hot reads!

Judd Sanders was a cop whose cover left him a little too
'uncovered' for his liking! And sweet Emily Cooper was
completely bemused by him; one minute, he was rescuing her
from muggers, the next, he was tearing off his clothes in front of
a crowd of voracious women...

THE HONEYMOON DEAL by Kate Hoffmann

Lianne Cooper had to ask her hunky ex-husband Mitch to play
the part of a madly-in-love newly wed so that she could assess
honeymoon locations. Trouble was, Mitch didn't seem to be
pretending... He'd become her perfect lover—cherishing her by
day and making slow passionate love to her through the night.

THE NEXT MAN IN TEXAS by Kristine Rolofson

Bachelors & Booties

Grace Daniels had been asked to take a baby to his father. But
'Daddy' could be any one of the four McLintock brothers. Jack,
the eldest, had spent the past fifteen years raising his brothers, he
definitely didn't want another baby...or the woman who came
with it!

POSSESSING ELISSA by Donna Sterling

Dreamscape

Captain Jesse Garrett was coming home... Back to the woman
he'd loved one passionate night, and the baby boy he'd never
seen. He was going to have to move heaven and earth for Elissa
and their son...

MILLS & BOON®

Christmas Treats

A sparkling new anthology
—the perfect Christmas gift!

Celebrate the season with a taste of love in this
delightful collection of brand-new short stories
combining the pleasures of food and love.

Figgy Pudding
by PENNY JORDAN
All the Trimmings
by LINDSAY ARMSTRONG
A Man For All Seasonings
by DAY LECLAIRE

And, as an extra treat, we've included the
authors' own recipe ideas in this
collection—because no yuletide would be
complete without...Christmas Dinner!

MILLS & BOON®

Season's Greetings
To all our readers!

The Season's Greetings Gift Pack brings you four
fabulous romances from star-studded authors
including Betty Neels.

And as an extra special Christmas treat we're
offering the pack at a discounted price of just
£6.60—that's 4 books for the price of 3.

The Mistletoe Kiss by Betty Neels
Merry Christmas by Emma Darcy
The Faithful Wife by Diana Hamilton
Home for Christmas by Ellen James

Available: November 1997

RISING
Tides

EMILIE RICHARDS

***The reading of a woman's will threatens to
destroy her family***

As a hurricane gathers strength, the reading of
Aurore Gerritsen's will threatens to expose dark
secrets and destroy her family. Emilie Richards
continues the saga of a troubled family with
Rising Tides, the explosive sequel to the critically
acclaimed *Iron Lace*.

**AVAILABLE IN PAPERBACK
FROM OCTOBER 1997**

JoAnn
ROSS

Southern Comforts

Welcome to Raintree, Georgia
—steamy capital of sin, scandal and murder

To her fans, Roxanne Scarborough is the queen of good
taste. To her critics she is Queen Bitch. And now somebody
wants her dead. When Chelsea Cassidy, Roxanne's official
biographer, begins to unearth the truth about Roxanne's life,
her investigation takes on a very personal nature—with
potentially fatal consequences.

"JoAnn Ross delivers a sizzling, sensuous romance."

—Romantic Times

 AVAILABLE NOW IN PAPERBACK

MISSING LINKS

How would you like to win a year's supply of Mills & Boon® books? Well you can and they're FREE! Simply complete the competition below and send it to us by 30th April 1998. The first five correct entries picked after the closing date will each win a year's subscription to the Mills & Boon series of their choice. What could be easier?

1. APPLE	P I E	CRUST
2. STRAWBERRY	_ _ _	TARTS
3. MINCED	_ _ _ _	BALLS
4. PICKLED	_ _ _ _ _	RING
5. GRAPE	_ _ _ _ _	JUICE
6. FRENCH	_ _ _ _ _	SAUCE
7. TOFFEE	_ _ _ _ _	CRUMBLE
8. PEANUT	_ _ _ _ _ _	BEANS
9. TANDOORI	_ _ _ _ _ _ _	CURRY
10. PRAWN	_ _ _ _ _ _ _ _	SAUSAGES

Please turn over for details of how to enter ⇨ ^{C7J}

HOW TO ENTER

There are ten missing words in our list overleaf. Each of the missing words must link up with the two words on either side to make a type of food.

For example, the word *Pie* links with *Apple* and *Crust* to form *Apple Pie* and *Pie Crust*:

APPLE - PIE - CRUST

As you find each one, write it in the space provided, we've done the first one for you! When you have linked up all the words, don't forget to fill in the coupon below, pop this page in an envelope and post it today—you don't even need a stamp!

Hurry, competition ends 30th April 1998.

Mills & Boon® Missing Links Competition
FREEPOST, Croydon, Surrey, CR9 3WZ

EIRE readers send competition to PO Box 4546, Dublin 24.

Please tick the series you would like to receive
if you are a winner:

Presents™ ❑ Enchanted™ ❑ Medical Romance™ ❑
Historical Romance™ ❑ Temptation® ❑

Are you a Reader Service™ Subscriber?　　Yes ❑　　No ❑

Ms/Mrs/Miss/Mr _____

(BLOCK CAPS PLEASE)

Address_____

_____

_____ Postcode_____

(I am over 18 years of age)　　　　　　　　　　　　　　　C7J